D0996831

PRINTING EXPLAINED

PRINTING EXPLAINED

AN ELEMENTARY PRACTICAL HANDBOOK

FOR SCHOOLS AND AMATEURS

BY

HERBERT SIMON

AND

HARRY CARTER

ILLUSTRATED BY

G. M. FREEBAIRN

LEICESTER:

THE DRYAD PRESS

3rd Impression : 1947

CONTENTS

FOREWORD

This is a book about a process—not about a product. It is, I believe, the first book of its kind in England since Johnson's *Typographia*, published in 1824, from which (but several years after its first publication) I learnt to set type. In the last ten years there have been published tome after tome about the aesthetics of printing, the function of printing, the history of printing, collection after collection of examples of fine printing; but, until this book, not a single book simply about *printing*—the process of combining types and taking impressions from them.

I lay emphasis on the word "process" for two reasons. The first is that the process of printing is in itself fascinating. It is difficult, but not too difficult; progress is quick, and easily measured; it lulls like knitting—it excites like a keen game; it makes one more aware of words, their sense and their structure, and more fond of them—even, believe me, of syllables and letters; and this process of printing plays up (if I may use that trivial expression where a specialised jargon is now so readily available) to certain definite psychological needs. It flatters one's importance as an individual, since almost every word sets a special, a private problem to the conscientious compositor; and at the same time it demands the nicest team-work. It makes one feel something of an artist, a poet, a maker and creator—although one has only the artist's desire and not his capacity. The process, in short, makes printing the best of hobbies—useful, flattering, fascinating.

But this process of printing, clearly and practically described in this book, is to be emphasised for another reason. Book designers, "layout" men, all of us who profess or practise printing, are much too apt to work backwards from the product. When we arrive at the process we find maybe that we have mistaken it. We gaze at the work of the great printers of the past, and we re-design our material—our types and our ornaments and our rules-of-thumb—to imitate their results. We may even have to "fake" our process, make a deliberate misuse of our equipment, to capture some no longer appropriate result.

This is the simple and extreme case against "period" printing, and for a return to process as a basis for design; but it stands for something much more elaborate. It stands for the possibilities of development and growth in printing styles. The cure for heavy conservatism is not to "call in" the artist. When he has been called in he has failed hopelessly of his job—because, in fact, it was *not* his job. He was ignorant of the process. The job, the process, the tools, the materials—these are your best artists.

It is, then, from those who will approach printing as a hobby, a process or a job that any growth in the styles of printing must come. It is one of the merits of this book that only one chapter is given to "design and lay-out," and in that chapter there is but one citation of historic practice.

It is the essential of a good hobby and of a true process that it should produce something useful and ornamental. Your fretwork photograph frame, or model engine, or carpentered corner-cupboard have no doubt been great fun to make, but their useful life is—forgive me—short or non-existent. These are not supplying inevitable needs. The school printer, on the other hand, has the enormous satisfaction of producing something which must otherwise be bought, let us say, from the jobbing office of the local newspaper. It is real, it is not play. More—he will in many cases soon be able to turn out a better job—more distinctive, simpler, more suited to its purpose—than those he has been buying. He will be able to meet and beat the professional. Of what other hobby can this be said?

FRANCIS MEYNELL

CHAPTER I

A CRAFT FOR SCHOOLS

A criticism frequently levelled against craft work in schools and against much amateur effort generally is one of the uselessness and comparative crudity of the finished work. Interest is quickened and industry intensified if, at the end, some useful object is made.

There must be difficulty in finding a craft where processes follow closely the normal routine of professional work, and where there is the definite utilitarian end of supplying goods which are wanted by a community. Printing may very well be such a pursuit. In a community such as a school the manual and mental training provided by printing can be turned to useful account by producing such everyday wants as programmes, notices, notepaper, invitation cards and even school magazines. The planning and production of real work will be found stimulating, and will bring forth a degree of enthusiasm and effort which must be rare in ordinary classroom projects.

Beyond kindling a spirit of enthusiasm on account of its usefulness, printing is also a fine example of group effort. Compositor, proof-reader, pressman and bookbinder combine their efforts towards the perfect result. That the results will, almost certainly, be imperfect when compared with professional work is of little account; for printing can be useful and well designed without having the polish of mechanical perfection.

Everyone who, as a novice, has become passionately interested in a skilled pursuit must have found that among its advantages is the critical appreciation of advanced work to which it leads. This is a great factor in education, for, while the uninstructed are always able to find fault, appreciation is a mark of more developed minds. Printers certainly always have an abundance of material at hand on which they can exercise their judgment. By doing so they are gradually led to slough off low standards of taste and efficiency and to feel discontented with their own past achievements. Mastery of any one craft develops a faculty of true criticism which can be exercised in many directions.

An advantage which seems peculiar to printing is its lack of finality. It is never too late to mend, and, in the mending, no material need be wasted. In many crafts poor work may be due to an initial mistake which is irretrievable; the best has to be made of a bad job or waste of valuable material has to be faced. Errors in the setting up of type or in the preparation on the printing-machine are not irreparable, and with reasonable patience and a high standard of attention to detail good, sound work is possible.

Type is a mere medium which can take shape in an endless variety of designs. This quality makes printing an admirable field for the encouragement of self-expression and development of an interest in design. Skill in drawing is not a necessary part of a printer's equipment, but the craft affords an opportunity for exercising a talent for artistic expression which would otherwise remain dormant through lack of technical ability.

Books are our constant companions and so urgent a need that it is curious to find how few seem to know the manner of their making. It happens that the working of a small private press does not differ in essentials from the tremendously complicated machinery of the professional office; this makes it possible to acquire a nodding acquaintanceship with the various mechanical operations that go to the making of books.

Printing helps to co-ordinate control over hand, eye and brain. Clumsy fingers are poor tools for setting type. There can be few more certain ways of making the fingers respond to the will than constant practice at the case. It is a training ground where confidence comes quickly; for the knowledge that mistakes are not irretrievable and that a fresh start can always be made must dispel those anxieties which haunt the nervous beginner.

To a good speller the fears and doubts of a bad speller must seem slightly absurd. It is indeed miserable to spell uncertainly and to feel shipwrecked when parted from a pocket dictionary. Printing concerns itself with spelling very intimately. Type is read as it is set up line by line; it is read in proof, and it is read again when the page is on the printing machine. The proof-reader is charged with the task of finding errors and investigating any doubtful points. Clearly, here is a task which calls for the most intensive study of words: it is one that may easily become the cradle of good spelling. Printing goes further than teaching spelling and punctuation; it is also a lesson in applied mathematics. Measuring type areas and finding the most economical way of cutting up sheets of paper to a smaller size are exercises which can claim equality with the less obviously useful task of finding the Greatest Common Factor.

In this book an attempt has been made to explain clearly how a printer sets about his work. It is mainly a practical exposition of type-setting, proof-reading, platen presswork and Albion presswork. A few specimen settings have been included, but there is no intention of showing in detail how work should be planned. This is impossible, as one of the glories of printing lies in the fact that every piece of work is in some part original and none is an exact prototype of another.

It is perhaps natural for printers to extol the virtues of their own craft. This may not be entirely unreasonable, for it is significant that, amongst professional workers, there is so commonly found a quickened interest and a spirit of venture which can only be present when the bogy of monotony has been banished.

It has been said recently that a defect in ordinary schooling is the slight attention given to the acquisition of manual skill. In this book we are dealing with an exercise to which manual dexterity is a first essential; but, what is more, all the faculties are being taught to act in harmony together. When the mind, eye and hand are working together they are acquiring a kind of skill which involves the whole being. It is just this that is needed to counteract the evils of the lack of balance in our civilisation due to a maladjustment of skill between the mind and the body.

CHAPTER 2

OUTLINE OF THE TECHNIQUE OF PRINTING

The kind of printing that we are concerned with in this book is printing from movable types, with illustrations considered more or less as accessory. We must rule out of our survey that process called "intaglio," in which the letters and the lines of a drawing are sunk into the medium instead of standing in relief as do type and blocks. Intaglio, which is used among other things for visiting cards and most music-printing, requires special apparatus of a kind that we do not deal with here. Lithography, or printing with ink, oil, and water from a flat surface of zinc or stone, is not included in the word "printing" as it is commonly used. We are only dealing here with taking impressions on paper from inked surfaces standing in relief.

Letterpress printing, as this work is called, is divided into two main departments — composing and presswork. Under the heading "composing" falls the arrangement of the type in words and lines, its formation into pages, the addition of headings and decoration, the arrangement of pages of type in solid rectangles to be put on the press, proof-reading and correction and, lastly, the distribution of the letters into the case after use.

"Presswork" is the process of taking impressions from type. It involves, besides the manipulation of the press or printing machine, the mixing and application of ink, the business called "make-ready," that is a matter of minute adjustments to obtain an equally strong impression from all the type, some-times damping the paper, and printing the type in the right position on the page.

Type is bought by weight from typefounders. Whatever may be the weight of a consignment of type, it is made up of all the necessary letters and signs in the right proportions, so that no one letter shall be used up much before the rest.

Printers keep their type in wooden trays, called "cases,"

divided up by partitions giving little compartments of varying sizes to hold the different characters. The cases, when in use, are laid on a kind of desk in front of which the compositor stands and, memorising two or three words of his manuscript, picks up one letter after another and arranges them in his composing-stick. The task of composing would be a much simpler and quicker one if there were not a rigid convention that lines must be all of the same length, so that the printed matter forms a perfect rectangle on the page. In order to conform with this convention, every line of type has to be "justified," that is, brought to the standard length by varying the spacing between words. The length of the lines, or "measure," is determined first of all, and the composing-stick is adjusted so that a line of the right measure will just fit into it. When the compositor has set a number of words with a space after each one and comes nearly to the end of the measure, he has to consider whether he will crowd another word in by putting less space between the words, or will space the words in the composing-stick further apart so that they will fill the measure, or will "break" the word, that is, put one syllable at the end of one line followed by a hyphen and the rest of the word at the beginning of the next line.

Books and pamphlets are, in commercial practice, set up completely from beginning to end, and the work is put for the time being in long metal trays, called "column galleys." The question of dividing the contents of the galleys into pages is left until the whole of the manuscript is set. The type remains in the galleys until proofs from it have been read and corrected by the printer's proof-reader and the author, and their directions for alterations carried out. If the type were made up into pages as the work went on, the corrections would often involve taking the last few lines from one page and putting them at the beginning of the next, or *vice versa,* thus upsetting all the pages throughout the book.

The amount which an amateur printer can set up at one time is of course limited by the quantity of his type. In non-commercial practice it is usual to set enough type for both sides of the largest sheet that the press will print, and to distribute the type as soon as the sheet is printed. In this way the press may be kept continuously at work. When the time comes for making the type into pages, enough lines to make a page are separated from the rest and the page-headings and the number of the page added to them. If there are illustrations these are inserted in the correct positions and each page of type is tied round with string.

The next stage is to wedge the pages into a frame, called a "chase," making a rigid unit that can be handled and put into the press. This process is known as "imposing." When there is a big press and many pages are printed at once, imposing becomes a complicated and somewhat difficult business. The unit consisting of several pages of type is called a "forme" and, of course, two formes are needed for each sheet, one for either side of the paper. The pairs of formes have to be arranged in such a way that when the sheet of paper is folded and the edges cut, the pages are in consecutive order. Imposition will not present much difficulty to owners of small platen presses, because the forme is not likely to contain more than two pages at a time. Their arrangement will not give rise to serious problems. Those who own Albion presses will be confronted with more difficult problems of imposition, since their formes may consist of eight pages or more. It is easy to make mistakes in imposing, and unless they are found out in time, all the copies of a sheet will have to be thrown away and a fresh lot printed. To avoid this risk, it is well to follow a plan taken from a book (plans for two, four, six and eight-page impositions are given on pp. 69-71), and to guard against mistakes in imposition by always folding and cutting a trial sheet before printing the rest.

The size of the sheet will depend on the number of pages needed for the job, the maximum capacity of the press, and the quantity of type available. In the class of work known to the trade as "jobbing," including such things as notices, leaflets, programmes and stationery, which will form the bulk of the printing done by school printers, the sheet will be designed to be just large enough for the work. In the case of booklets the sheet will be the largest that the press and the supply of type will allow. A sheet of 15 in. × 10 in., printed on both sides, requires from 40 to 50 lb. of type.

The sizes of books take their names from the number of folds in the sheets of which they are made. Quarto means

folded into four; octavo, into eight, and so on. It is conven-
tionally supposed that the sheet is a full sheet, the largest
which the old-fashioned wooden presses would take. Full
sheets are made in several sizes, *e.g.* Crown 15 in. × 20in.;
Demy 17½ in. × 22½ in.; Medium 18 in. × 23 in.; Royal 20 in.
× 25 in., etc. Therefore, the size of the folded section of a
book is correctly described as Crown quarto, Demy octavo,
Royal sextodecimo (or "sixteenmo"). In actual practice sheets
are not always full sheets, they are often four or eight times
as big; hand-made papers are generally Demy or Royal; while
the machine-made are commonly Double-Crown 20 in. ×
30 in.; Double-Demy 22½ in. × 35 in.; Double-Royal 25 in.
× 40 in.; for writing-papers used for stationery Foolscap
(13½ in. × 17 in.) and Large Post (16½ in. × 21 in.) are
usual sizes. School printers will be obliged by the smallness
of their presses to use sheets cut in sections, but the page will
still take its name from the full sheet out of which it was cut.
The largest page that can be printed on the platen press
recommended in this book, whose chase measures 7½ in. ×
5 in., will be small Royal octavo (9 in. × 6 in.), for the type-area
of a Royal octavo page would never exceed 7½ in. × 5 in.

Even though the sheet is only a part of the full sheet, the
fact that it is an octavo or a quarto or a sixteenmo makes a
difference to the imposition, because in sewing the sheets into
a book it will be found unsatisfactory to sew one sheet at a
time on to the tapes that hold the book together. It will be
necessary to sew through at least two sheets at once to prevent
tearing the paper, and better to sew through three or four at
a time. Therefore, when printing booklets the sheets will
have to be arranged to fit one inside another or, as printers
express it, the sheets will be "quired." Suppose that the unit
to be sewn together is a booklet or section of a book consisting
of eight pages and they are octavos, then page 1 will be printed
on the first sheet, page 2 on the back of it, page 3 will go on
the second sheet, page 4 on the back of 3, 5 on the same side
of the same sheet beside 4, 6 on the back of 5, 7 will come
on the first sheet beside 2, and 8 beside 1 on the back of 3.
(It is a rigid convention among printers that odd-numbered
pages should come on the right-hand side of an open book.)
It will only be found possible to print each page as soon as

it is set up if a single page is put in the press at a time. If it is desired to print two sixteenmo pages instead of one octavo in the platen press, then it will be necessary to set the type of all the pages that are to be sewn together before beginning to print. This is because it is impossible (in the case of continuous matter) to set page 8 until page 7 is finished, or indeed any page until the preceding one is done, because the compositor would not know at which point of the manuscript to begin the page unless he could tell where the preceding page ended. For this reason, if school printers desire to print a book or booklet in Royal sixteenmo, they must buy enough type to print both sides of a Royal quarto, that is, about 35 to 40 lb.

If the press used be a small Albion, let us say with a Foolscap folio sized platen (14 in. × 9 in.), the largest sheet that can be printed will be a Crown folio.

Having laid down the pages of type in the right order the printer proceeds to "dress" the two formes for printing the two sides of his sheet. He puts strips of wood between the pages to keep them far enough apart to make margins on the printed sheet round each page. He puts the iron or steel frame or chase round the imposed pages and wedges the type and wooden "furniture" tightly into it, so that the whole thing becomes quite rigid and will not fall to pieces when picked up.

One forme is put in the press and a trial imposition is taken. The correct position for laying the sheet is found experimentally, and pieces of metal are gummed on the packing of the platen as a guide for the pressman in putting the sheets in. After printing the required number of copies, the forme for the other side of the paper is put in the press. Trials have to be made with the second forme to make the impression from it "register" with that from the first so that the pages come exactly back-to-back. The register is judged by holding the sheet up to the light to see whether the pages on either side coincide. If they are printed in bad register the fault will generally be visible because paper is seldom quite opaque.

When the sheet is printed on both sides it is left for a time to dry before being folded and sewn up in sections.

This, in very rough outline, is the technique of letterpress printing. In the following chapters it is explained in more detail with practical directions for beginners.

CHAPTER 3

EQUIPMENT

Before venturing into printing the cost of the equipment required must be known. This information must be available before any decision can be made. We will therefore go into the question of cost and give a schedule of the precise material that is necessary to start a press.

Unless a substantial sum of money is forthcoming, printing can only be carried on by a few persons at a time. Its position is very similar to the carpenter's craft, where only a limited number of workers can be engaged in producing at the same time unless the tools and benches are duplicated many times over. It is indeed preferable that classes should be of limited size; a small class can work together better as a team and more readily combine their efforts towards an efficient production. Printing has a decided advantage over some other pursuits in that, when once the equipment has been installed, the cost of raw materials and general running expenses are very small.

In preparing schemes of equipment considerable care has been taken to select materials of good quality which will wear well and give excellent service over a very long period. Provided reasonable treatment is meted out to the plant, there should be few expenses for renewals beyond the re-clothing of printing-machine rollers and the provision of such "stores" as small amounts of cleaning material and printer's ink.

The prices given in the following lists are only approximate and useful as a general guide.

For £60 it is possible to provide a modestly equipped office which will give work for at least four printers; £150 will buy a much more completely equipped office, which will give work to a class of six or more persons. Distribution of labour is a principle which must be recognised. In the larger printing office four compositors will be setting type; one will be occupied in proof-reading and attending at the imposing-surface where the pages of type are locked up in chases;

THE £40 EQUIPMENT

Item	Description	s.	d.	£	s.	d.
1	30 lb. 10-point Caslon Old Face .. .. per lb.	4	2	6	5	0
2	5 lb. 10-point Caslon Old Face *Italic* .. ,,	4	3	1	1	3
3	30 lb. 12-point Caslon Old Face .. .. ,,	3	9	5	12	6
4	5 lb. 12-point Caslon Old Face *Italic* .. ,,	3	10		19	2
5	10 lb. 18-point Caslon Titling .. .. ,,	2	8	1	6	8
6	6 lb. 10-point Spaces .. .. ,,	1	8		10	0
7	3 lb. 10-point Quads .. .. .. ,,	1	3		3	9
8	6 lb. 12-point Spaces .. .. .. ,,	1	4		8	0
9	3 lb. 12-point Quads .. .. .. ,,		11		2	9
10	2 lb. 18-point Spaces .. .. .. ,,	1	4		2	8
11	2 lb. 18-point Quads .. .. .. ,,		10		1	8
12	2 lb. 10-point Borders .. .. .. ,,	5	6		11	0
13	14 lb. Metal Furniture assorted 24-, 36- and 48-point by 4 to 24 ems .. .. ,,		10		11	8
14	14 lb. 1½-point Leads assorted lengths: 6 to 24 ems .. .. ,,		10		11	8
15	Setting-rules in box		—		6	0
16	Single Frame to accommodate 12 cases ..		—	2	15	0
17	Six Double Cases .. .. each 9 6			2	17	0
18	One Lead Case		—		9	0
19	Slate Imposing Surface, 10½ in. × 14 in. ..		—		5	3
20	Six lengths 6-point Reglets		—			9
21	Six lengths 12-point Reglets		—		1	0
22	Cutting above into lengths 6 to 24 ems rising by 2 ems		—		1	6
23	Three lengths 24-point Wood Furniture ..		—			8
	Three lengths 36-point Wood Furniture ..		—			10
	Three lengths 48-point Wood Furniture ..		—		1	0
24	Cutting and numbering above into the following lengths : 6 to 24 ems rising by 2 ems.. ..		—		3	9
25	Two 6 in. steel Composing-sticks .. each 9 6				19	0
26	Three pressed steel Galleys 13 in.×8¾ in. ,, 1 9				5	3
27	Twelve pairs small plain Hempel Quoins ..		—		2	4
28	One Key for quoins		—		2	0
29	Tweezers and Palette Knife		—		4	0
30	Page Cord and Type Brush		—		3	6
31	Small thin Planer and Mallet		—		5	3
32	Paraffin Sprinkler		—		3	6
33	Light Card and Paper Cutter 10¼ in. ..		—	1	0	0
34	Six bearers for locking in chases		—		3	0
35	No. 2 Platen Press for hand—7½ in. × 5 in. inside chase, two inkers, one chase, spanners, etc. ..		—	10	0	0
	TOTAL			£38	17	4

Prices have risen since these lists were prepared. It would be prudent to add 50% for an estimation of present costs.

THE £100 EQUIPMENT

Item	Description		s.	d.	£	s.	d.
	Type and Brass Rule						
1	25 lb. 10-point Caslon Old Face .. .. per lb.		4	2	5	4	2
2	10 lb. 10-point Caslon Old Face *Italic* .. ,,		4	3	2	2	6
3	50 lb. 12-point Caslon Old Face .. ,,		3	9	9	7	6
4	20 lb. 12-point Caslon Old Face *Italic* .. ,,		3	10	3	16	8
5	20 lb. 14-point Caslon Old Face .. ,.		3	5	3	8	4
6	10 lb. 14-point Caslon Old Face *Italic* .. ,,		3	5	1	14	2
7	25 lb. 18-point Caslon Titling .. ,,		2	8	3	6	8
8	25 lb. 24-point Caslon Titling .. ,,		2	8	3	6	8
9	30 lb. 36-point Caslon Titling .. ,,		2	8	4	0	0
10	12 lb. 10-point Spaces .. .. .. ,,		1	8	1	0	0
11	7 lb. 10-point Quads .. .. .. ,,		1	1		7	7
12	12 lb. 12-point Spaces .. .. .. ,,		1	4		16	0
13	7 lb. 12-point Quads .. .. .. ,,			11		6	5
14	7 lb. 14-point Spaces .. .. .. ,.		1	4		9	4
15	4 lb. 14-point Quads .. .. .. ,.			11		3	8
16	3 lb. 18-point Spaces .. .. .. ,,		1	4		4	0
17	3 lb. 18-point Quads .. .. .. ,,			10		2	6
18	3 lb. 24-point Spaces .. .. .. ,,		1	4		4	0
19	3 lb. 24-point Quads .. .. .. ,			10		2	6
20	4 lb. 36-point Spaces .. .. .. ,		1	4		5	4
21	4 lb. 36-point Quads .. .. .. ,			10		3	4
22	1 lb. 8-point Border .. .. .. ,.			—		6	2
23	2 lb. 10-point Border .. .. .. ,,		5	6		11	0
24	2 lb. 12-point Border .. .. .. ,,		5	0		10	0
25	2 lb. 14-point Border .. .. .. ,.		4	10		9	8
26	2 lb. 18-point Border .. .. .. ,.		3	10		7	8
27	28 lb. Metal Furniture assorted 24-, 36- and 48-point by 4 to 24 ems .. .. ,,			10	1	3	4
28	28 lb. 1½-point Leads assorted lengths, 6 to 24 ems .. .. ,,			8½		19	10
29	2-point medium face Brass Rule (bevelled one side), 486 pieces assorted, 1 to 36 ems .			—	1	16	0
30	One labour-saving set 2-point Full Face Brass Rule, comprising the following pieces : Eight pieces each ½, 1¼, 1½, 2, 3, 3½, 4, 4½ and 5 ems; Ten pieces each 6, 8, 10, 12, 15 and 18 ems; Eight pieces each 20 and 24 ems; Eight pairs each 6, 3 and 2 em mitred pieces			—		16	6
	Wood Material and Sundries						
31	Two Single Frames, each with rack for 12 cases to accommodate the following .. .. each	55	0	5	10	0
	Twelve Improved Double Cases .. .. ,,	9	6	5	14	0
	Carried Forward				£58	13	6

THE £100 EQUIPMENT (*continued*)

Item	Description		s.	d.	£	s.	d.
	Wood Material and Sundries (continued)						
	Brought Forward				58	13	6
	Four Upper Cases	each	8	o	1	12	o
	One Brass Rule Case		—			14	o
	Two Lead Cases	each	9	o		18	o
	One Open Case		—			6	o
	One Border Case		—			10	6
	One Metal Furniture Case		—			9	6
	Two Cases for Reglet and Wood Furniture	each	9	6		19	o
32	One iron Imposing-surface 12 in. × 18 in. ..		—		1	15	o
33	Twelve lengths 6-point Reglet		—			1	6
34	Twelve lengths 12-point Reglet		—			1	9
35	Cutting above as follows :						
	Sixteen pieces each 6-point and 12-point in the following lengths : 6 to 24 ems rising by 2 ems (320 pieces in all) .. .. at per 100		10			2	8
36	Three lengths 24-point Wood Furniture at per doz.		2	6			8
	Three lengths 36-point Wood Furniture „		3	6			10
	Three lengths 48-point Wood Furniture „		4	o		1	o
	Three lengths 72-point Wood Furniture „		5	o		1	3
37	Cutting and numbering above as follows :						
	Four pieces each 24-, 36-, 48- and 72-point in the following lengths : 6 to 24 ems rising by 2 ems .. .. .. at per 100		2	6		4	o
38	One small thin Planer		—			2	9
39	One Mallet		—			2	6
40	Twelve pairs small plain Hempel Quoins ..		—			2	4
41	One Key for ditto		—			2	o
42	Six pressed steel Galleys, 13 in. × 8¾ in. each		1	9		10	6
43	Two mahogany and steel Jobbing Galleys, 8½ in. × 5½ in. .. .. each		3	6		7	o
44	Two 6 in. stainless steel Composing-sticks, each		9	6		19	o
45	Two 8 in. stainless steel Composing-sticks, each		12	o	1	4	o
46	Setting Rules		—			7	6
47	One Palette Knife		—			2	6
48	Page-cord and Type Brush		—			3	6
49	Two pairs Tweezers		—			2	6
50	Paraffin Sprinkler		—			3	6
51	Card and Paper Cutter (12½ in.)		—		2	o	o
52	Six Bearers for locking in chases		—			3	6
	Platen Machine						
53	One treadle-operated Platen Press, 8 in. × 5 in. inside chase, fitted with three inking rollers, two chases, ink-duct, spanners, etc.		—		25	o	o
	TOTAL				£98	4	3

Prices have risen since these lists were prepared. It would be prudent to add 50% for an estimation of present costs.

another worker will be wanted to operate the printing machine, and yet another to distribute back into the cases type which is no longer required. If an Albion press is used it will have to be operated by two persons. The smaller printing office, which is much weaker in types and cases, will not be able to

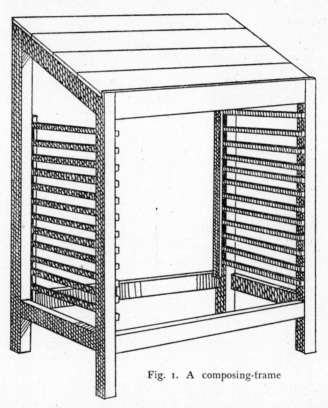

Fig. 1. A composing-frame

accommodate more than two compositors, but it will want, also, the machine-minder and reader and, perhaps, a distributor of type.

If a school has a carpenter's shop it can be of great assistance to the printing-press. Skeleton composing frames can be constructed without great difficulty, as shown in Figure 1. On the tops of these frames type cases can be placed and more compositors may be set to work. Cast iron brackets can be bought for a small sum which will convert a flat-topped piece of furniture

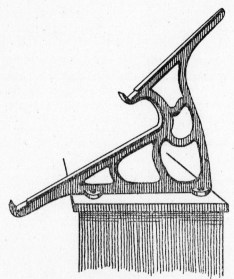

into a composing-frame. Carpenters can also make a support for the imposing-surface (Figure 3), tables for paper, a cupboard for ink and stores, and boxes for storing printing machine rollers.

The question may be asked—is printing safe? The answer is that it is perfectly safe provided ordinary standards of care are observed. There

Fig. 2. Bracket for type cases

is every reason to think that the chance of injury is much less than in a handicraft where fretwork or wood-carving tools are used. Fingers can be caught and lacerated in large printing-presses, and powerful paper-cutting machines are exceedingly dangerous unless they are operated by skilled labour; but machines of this kind do not come within the range of the proposed equipments. The press is slow-running and small and cannot damage fingers; the paper-cutter is operated with safety, as the paper clamp has to be held down with the left hand whilst the right hand pulls over the cutting lever.

Some people are under the impression that there is a danger of lead-poisoning from the constant handling of type. This is fallacious; lead-poisoning, even amongst professional compositors, is quite unknown. The trade is not scheduled as a "dangerous trade." Type and printer's ink make hands grimy, and it will be as natural as it is desirable to wash thoroughly after a spell of work. Most people have an exaggerated horror of printer's ink; as a matter of fact it is very easy to wash off with soap and water.

Setting very small type undoubtedly imposes a strain on the eyes. In order to avoid any possibility of damaging the eyes, no letters smaller than 10-point have been allowed in the equipment. Every effort should be made to place the printing office in a bright room. Compositors are grateful for all the daylight they are given. Where possible, the composing-frames should be placed near windows. The printing-machine is not very heavy and can be set down on any reasonably good floor without fear of a disaster similar

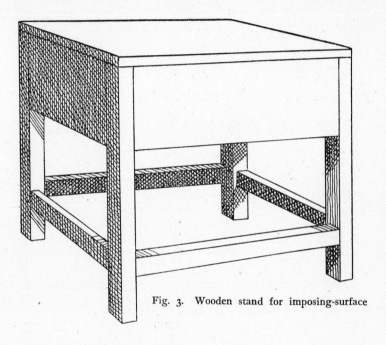

Fig. 3. Wooden stand for imposing-surface

to that which overtook Mr. Clayhanger's "Steam Printer" in the Five Towns. The plan opposite is a suggestion for the layout of an office.

It has been considered advisable to concentrate more on materials for type-setting to the partial eclipse of presswork. There is more likelihood of amateurs becoming good compositors, and the variety of approach which is possible in this section of the work seems to make it singularly suitable as an educative medium. Presswork is indeed extremely important, but its qualities are much more mechanical. Whilst a fairly high standard of presswork can be achieved, yet it is difficult, even on full-sized machines, to get results which are comparable to good professional work. The wide experience necessary for good presswork is normally beyond the reach of an amateur, and he must be content to labour under a slight disadvantage. Consequently, even in the larger equipment, quite a modest size of press has been recommended. For a

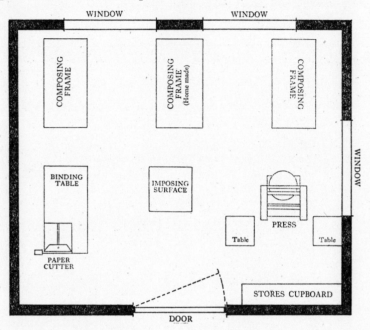

Fig. 4. Plan for a small printing-office

supplementary expenditure of about £20 a more efficient and larger press can be obtained. These presses are of heavy construction and have a very powerful impression, which is of great assistance in printing large pages of type. But the mechanics of both the small and the large presses are similar and follow closely in operation the practice of the "trade."

Although Caslon Old Face type is specified in the equipments, it must not be considered that this style of type is recommended to the exclusion of all others. Equally good for the purpose are Cloister Old Style or Baskerville. The merits of these three faces can be judged from the specimens on pages 23-25.

Typefounders cast a tempting array of ornamental borders. Many of them are quite unsuitable as typographic material, and do not seem to be related to the types with which they are intended to be used. The following designs have been carefully selected to accord with the type faces which have been recommended:

SPECIMENS OF ORNAMENTS

No. 1. 18-point

No. 2. 18-point

No. 3. 14-point

No. 4. 14-point.

No. 5. 12-point

No. 6. 12-point

No. 7. 12-point

No. 8. 10-point

No. 9. 8-point

No. 10. 8-point

CASLON, 12-point

At length I spied a little cove on the right shore of the creek, to which, with great pain and difficulty, I guided my raft, and at last got so near, as that, reaching ground with my oar, I could thrust her directly in; but here I had like to have dipped all my cargo in the sea again; for that shore lying pretty steep, that is to say, sloping, there was no place to land but where one end of my float, if it run on shore, would lie so high and the other sink lower, as before, that it would endanger my cargo again. All that I could do was to wait till the tide was at the highest, keeping the *raft with my oar like an anchor to hold the side of it fast to the shore, near a flat piece of ground, which I expected the water would flow over; and so it did. As soon as I found water enough, for my raft drew about a foot of water, I thrust her on upon that flat piece of ground, and there fastened or moored her*

CASLON, 10-point

My next work was to view the country and seek a proper place for my habitation, and where to stow my goods to secure them from whatever might happen. Where I was, I yet knew not; whether on the continent, or on an island; whether inhabited, or not inhabited; whether in danger of wild beasts, or not. There was a hill, not above a mile from me, which rose up very steep and high, and which seemed to overtop some other hills, which lay as in a ridge from it, northward. I took out one of the fowling-pieces and one of the pistols, and a horn of powder; and thus armed, I travelled for discovery up to the top of that hill, where, after I had with great labour and difficulty got to the top, I saw my fate to my great affliction, viz., that I was in an island environed every way with the sea, no land to be seen, except some rocks which lay a great way off, and two small islands less than this, which lay about three leagues to the west.

I found also that the island I was in was barren, and, as I saw good reason *to believe, uninhabited, except by wild beasts, of whom, however, I saw none; yet I saw abundance of fowls, but knew not their kinds; neither, when I killed them, could I tell what was fit for food, and what not. At my coming back, I shot a great bird which I saw sitting upon a tree on the side of a great wood. I believe it was the first gun that had been fired there since the*

CLOISTER, 12-point

I got on board the ship as before, and prepared a second raft and having had experience of the first, I neither made this so unwieldly, nor loaded it so hard; but yet I brought away several things very useful to me; as, first, in the carpenter's stores I found two or three bags full of nails and spikes, a great screw-jack, a dozen or two of hatchets, and above all, that most useful thing called a grindstone. All these I secured, otgether with several things belonging to the gunner, particularly two or three iron crows, and two barrels of musket bullets, seven muskets, and another fowling-piece, with some small quantity of powder more; *a large bag full of small-shot, and a great roll of sheet lead; but this last was so heavy, I could not hoist it up to get it over the ship's side. Besides these things, I took all the men's clothes that I could find, and a spare fore-top sail, a hammock, and some bedding; and with this I loaded my second raft, and brought them all safe on shore, to my very great comfort.*

CLOISTER, 10-point

I was under some apprehensions during my absence from the land, that at least my provisions might be devoured on shore; but when I came back, I found no sign of any visitor, only there sat a creature like a wild cat upon one of the chests, which, when I came towards it, ran away a little distance, and then stood still. She sat very composed and unconcerned, and looked full in my face, as if she had a mind to be acquainted with me. I presented my gun at her; but as she did not understand it, she wsa perfectly unconcerned at it, nor did she offer to stir away; upon which I tossed her a bit of biscuit, though, by the way, I was not very free of it, for my store was not great. However, I spared her a bit, I say, and she went to it, smelled of it, and ate it, and looked (as pleased) for more; but I thanked her, and could spare no more, so she marched off.

Having got my second cargo on shore, though I was fain to open the barrels of powder and bring them by parcels, for they were too haevy, being large *casks, I went to work to make me a little tent with the sail and some poles which I cut for that purpose; and into this tent I brought everything that I knew would spoil either with rain or sun; and I piled all the empty chests and casks up in a circle round the tent, to fortify it from any sudden attempt, either from man or beast.*

When I had done this I blocked up the door of the tent with some boards within,

BASKERVILLE, 12-pt.

When the day of execution is come, among extraordinary sinners and persons condemned for their crimes, who have but that morning to live, one would expect a deep sense of sorrow, with all the signs of a thorough contrition, and the utmost concern; that either gravity or a sober silence should prevail; and that all, who had business there, should be grave and serious, and behave themselves, at least with decency, and a deportment suitable to the occasion. But the very reverse is true. The horrid aspects of turnkeys and gaolers, in discontent and hurry; the sharp and dread *looks of rogues, that beg in irons, but would rob you with greater satisfaction, if they could; the bellowings of half a dozen names at a time, that are perpetually made in the inquiries after one another; the variety of strong voices, that are heard, of howling in one place, scolding and quarrelling in another, and loud laugh-*

BASKERVILLE, 10-pt.

But what is most shocking to a thinking man, is the behaviour of the condemned, whom (for the most part) you'll find, either drinking madly, or uttering the vilest ribaldry, and jeering others, that are less impenitent; whilst the ordinary bustles among them, and shifting from one to another, distributes scraps of good counsel to unattentive hearers; and near him, the Hangman, impatient to be gone, swears at their delays, and, as fast as he can, does his part, in preparing them for their journey.

At last, out they set; and with them a torrent of mob bursts through the gate. Amongst the lower rank and working people, the idlest, and such as are most fond of making holidays, with prentices and journeymen to the meanest trades, are the most honourable of these floating multitudes. All the rest are worse. The days being known beforehand, *they are a summons to all thieves and pickpockets of both sexes to meet. Great mobs are a safeguard to one another, which makes these days Jubilees, on which old offenders, and all who dare not shew their heads on any other, venture out of their holes; and they resemble free marts, where there is an amnesty for all out-*

Note: The italic shown with Baskerville is known as "Georgian Old Face"

No provision has been made in either of the equipments for a proofing-press. They are expensive, and a home-made contrivance will give sufficiently good service. Thick felt secured to a piece of hardwood about 8 in. × 5 in. can be used to get an impression without much danger of damaging the type. This method of taking proofs is described in Chapter 5. Type which is to be proofed can be inked by one of the machine rollers; but if the press is busy and the rollers cannot be spared, a small hand roller can be purchased for a modest sum.

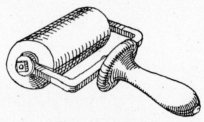

Fig. 5. An ink-roller

NOTE. *It is impossible to give a price for an Albion press, for these can best be bought in the second-hand market. The value of one with a folio-sized platen ranges from about £10 to £15.*

CHAPTER 4

COMPOSITION

The initial step in the mastery of the art of setting type is nothing less than a fairly severe memory test. The arrangement of the case has to be learnt, and the accompanying diagram must be committed to memory. The "case" is a shallow drawer, divided up into compartments of varying

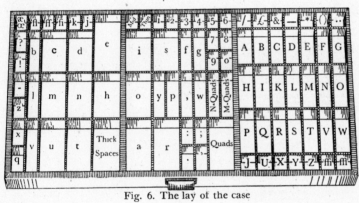

Fig. 6. The lay of the case

size, for the reception of the letters of the alphabet, figures, punctuation marks and spaces.

Not only has provision to be made for the capital letters, but a second alphabet has to be carried for the small, or lower-case letters. Reference to the diagram will show that the two complementary alphabets are housed in the same case. It is a model which is used in most modern printing offices, but it is of comparatively recent origin. Previously the capitals were placed in a separate case called the "upper case" and the small letters in a companion case called the "lower case" Hence, the printing terms "upper- and lower-case" characters. We are not recommending amateurs to stock small capitals (A, B, C, D, E, etc.), but if they do so they will have to provide themselves with an extra case.

It will be noticed that the compartments of the case are not of uniform size. This is because certain letters occur more frequently than others, and the partitioning of the case has made provision for this. The case-plan, called by printers the "lay of the case," has come down to us from very early days. The curious positions of U and J—at the end of the alphabet of capitals—show how old it is; printers have been too conservative to alter their stations since capital U and J came into use late in the sixteenth century. In all countries that use the roman alphabet the position of the commonest letters is the same, because their cases are all descended from a common ancestor, the arrangement devised by the early printers for setting Latin. Although in England, as in other countries, the case has been modified in detail to suit the local language, our case still has features due to its Latin origin, the excessively large box for c and the inconvenient box for w for example. Still, in the main it is a satisfactory arrangement.

The lower-case e is used more frequently than any other letter in the alphabet, and consequently it has been allotted the largest compartment, which has been specially placed for ease of access. Diphthongs, the lower-case k, j and z are rarely used, so they have to be content with a small compartment and a back seat in the case.

A study of the lay of the case will probably give rise to uncertainty about inverted commas. Inverted commas at the opening of a quotation are merely ordinary commas (,,) turned round ("); two apostrophes are used for closing a quotation, and they are kept in the compartment immediately on the right of the full point (.).

When it is felt that the lay of the case has been memorised, practice should begin with picking up letters from the case itself. We have to become accustomed to the feel of type. A few short words should be written out on a slip of paper and the necessary letters picked out. Each letter should be examined carefully and then put back again in its correct compartment. There is no need whatever for any haste at this early stage, but the exercise should be carried on quite deliberately until there is sufficient confidence that any letter called for can be picked out with accuracy. Normally, an aggregate of about four hours of this practice will produce a feeling of confidence. To some the lay of the case may come more easily if pieces of cardboard, inscribed with the letter for each particular box, are placed in the case and used for practice. The cardboard dummies will probably assist a slow learner.

Type is taken out of the case letter by letter and set in lines in the composing-stick. Before starting work the width of the line must be determined. The printer's unit of linear measurement is a "pica em." This is the colloquial name for 12 points, the equivalent of one-sixth of an inch, and therefore there are six pica ems to the inch. If it has been decided to set the lines to 18 ems (3 inches) the composing-stick must be adjusted to this measurement. It will be observed that

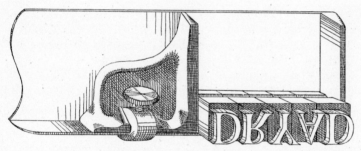

Fig. 7. A composing-stick

there is, on the composing-stick, a movable piece which can be made to slide up and down the length of the stick at right angles to the long back wall. This movable arm can be locked fast in any position desired by the turn of a thumb-screw.

It is immensely important that the slide be set accurately. If the measure is 18 ems, eighteen em-quads of 12-point type should be placed in the stick and the slide moved gently against them and then locked fast. This is the best method of fixing the measure because it provides a standard that is the same for all engaged on the same job; but it is quicker (and in practice satisfactory) to use a piece of brass rule of the correct length. There should be hardly any pressure of the slide on the type or rule which is acting as a gauge. If the stick is correctly set it should be just possible to lift out the type or the rule without using force. If the rule is being pressed so firmly that it bows, then the adjustment is too tight.

The compositor .now selects a setting-rule of the right length and puts it along the back of his composing-stick so that the letters rest against it and not against the steel wall of the stick. When a line of type is set and justified, the setting-rule is lifted out and put in front of the letters to provide a smooth surface for the succeeding line to rest against. Without a setting-rule it is difficult to justify the new line, since the line of type previously set prevents the letters from sliding sideways freely as the spacing between them is altered.

Setting-rules are sold cut to all the usual measures. In an emergency one may be made out of brass rule. Those made for the purpose are much preferable however, since their shape makes them easy to pull out of the stick while fitting closely into it, and their stout build is an advantage when they are used to support type as it is lifted out of the composing-stick and taken to the galley.

The compositor should stand squarely in front of the case and pick up the letters, one at a time, with the forefinger and thumb of the right hand.

Fig. 8. Setting-rule

The letters are transferred immediately to the stick, which is held in the left hand. The diagram demonstrates how the stick should be held. The under side rests between the thumb and forefinger and the open side of the stick is tilted up so that the letters will fall back for support on the back wall and not be in danger of falling over and dropping out of the open side of the stick. The left thumb is brought right round to the top of the open side, while the remaining fingers lend general support to the back.

In picking up the letters and depositing them in the stick experienced compositors work at an astonishing speed. But there is no need to emulate these professionals. The groundwork will be more thorough if accuracy takes precedence over speed. Nevertheless, all movements which help efficiency must be cultivated. When setting type, the right and the left hands should work in unison. This implies that the left hand, carrying the stick, must follow the movements of the

right as it darts over the case from compartment to compartment; by so doing the distance that the right hand has to
travel to find the stick is reduced to a minimum. When both
hands are following each other (after practice quite subcon-
sciously) it is remarkable how rhythmic type-setting can be.
The movements will become much smoother when the
compositor has learnt to "sight" the letters. In any one
compartment there will probably be at least a dozen types,

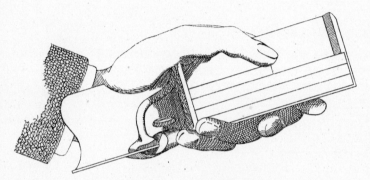

Fig. 9. How to hold the composing-stick

all of which would serve the purpose equally well, but there
should be no hesitation as to which should be picked up.
The compartment should be sighted and an individual type
selected and picked up to the exclusion of all others. As
experience increases "sighting" will become automatic, but
beginners must take care to practise it continually.

As each letter is withdrawn from the case and placed in the
stick it should be turned round so that the nick is pointing
outwards and will still be visible when the letter is placed up
against the setting-rule, which is acting as a template for the
measure. The nicks of successive letters should, when in the
stick, make a continuous line, which is an indication to the
compositor that the letters are facing the correct way. Should
the line of the nicks be broken (unless by the inverted commas
at the beginning of a quotation), then it may be assumed that
a letter has been turned round the wrong way; this requires
immediate rectification.

When the same letter occurs twice in succession do not try to pick two out of the case at once; they will seldom come up with the nicks right, and it causes delay.

As each letter is placed in the stick the thumb of the left hand must be brought against it to hold it in position until the next letter is in its place. Obviously, the letters require this support whilst the stick is moving in the track of the right hand.

After each word is set a thick space is inserted. There are three thick spaces to the em and it may be taken as a standard of spacing between words, although it is a standard which cannot be adherred to rigidly, as will be shown presently.

If a type-written letter is examined it will be noticed that the lines do not end evenly at the right-hand edge. This practice is not customary in printing, where lines have to be flush at both the right- and the left-hand edges. To arrange for this, the lines of type have to be very carefully and intelligently spaced out. This is known as justification.

Justification is so extremely important that it must be explained as fully as possible. There are two main factors in spacing which affect this process. In the first place the words of a line must be so spaced that no one-syllable word is divided and no long word broken at the wrong place. Secondly, the spaces between individual words in a line must be optically even. When the compositor sets the last word in the line the final distribution of the spaces must be considered. If the thick space has been used as a standard and, for example, the e of the word "the" will not fit into the measure, then the thick spaces will have to be removed and replaced by middle spaces (four to one em). By thus reducing the spacing and so bringing the words closer, room will be made for an additional letter and the word can be completed. (The quickest way to remove a wrong space is to knock it over with the end of the new space that is to take its place.) Conversely, it may be desirable to push one or two letters of an incomplete word on to the succeeding line and, in this event, instead of being decreased, the spacing must be opened out by the substitution of a middle and a thin for every thick space.

In justifying it is preferable not to use hair-spaces because they break or get bent. For example, you require a space thicker than a thick: do not insert a hair space, but use a middle and a thin, which give the same result. The following list gives the usual spaces in descending order of size:

> An em-quad (called a "mutton")
> Two thicks
> A thick and a middle
> An en-quad (called a "nut")
> A middle and a thin
> Two thins
> A thick
> A middle
> A thin
> A hair

Besides finding solutions for the correct division of words or for accommodating words of one syllable, the need for optically even spacing must not be overlooked. In the alphabet there are some letters which follow quite closely one another's contours, and there are others which seem to curve away from each other. A lower-case e or w followed by a c has naturally more white intervening than an l followed by a b. Adjustment in spacing must be made to meet these cases. Compare the following examples:

new variety of hard hat
(thick)   (thick) (thick)   (thick)
(all thick spaces: 3 to 1 em)

new variety of hard hat
(middle)   (middle) (thick)   (thick)
(optically even spacing: thick and middle spaces)

Even in professional composition it is not always possible to end lines correctly and at the same time do justice to optical spacing. But it is an ideal which must be aimed at constantly and achieved whenever possible.

Justification is not complete with the spacing out of the line. An essential point is to ensure that all lines in the stick fit with the same degree of tightness. It is not to be supposed that the lines must be so firmly wedged into the stick that it requires some tool to force the last space down into position The lines must be neither loosely nor tightly packed; but they should fit sufficiently closely to prevent lateral play between the letters, yet it must not be difficult to withdraw a line from the stick. Time and care must be given to justifying lines evenly, and it will be rewarded when the subsequent operations of imposition and machining are carried out.

The ordinary composing-stick is 6 in. to 12 in. long and about 1¾ in. from back to front. Consequently, after every six or seven lines have been set they must be lifted out of the stick and placed on a galley. Lifting lines of type from the stick demands both skill and caution. Pressure must be exerted so as to keep the lines firm and to prevent a "pie," which is a printer's term for a disaster in which the types tumble over and fall into a heap of complete confusion. Before lifting type from the stick put the stick down, with the open side furthest away from you, on a galley or on some convenient place on the slope of the frame. Put a lead of the correct measure between the wall of the stick and the first line, and

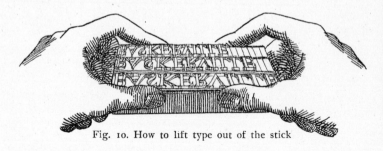

Fig. 10. How to lift type out of the stick

the setting-rule outside the last line set; these will keep the lines in place. Making use of both hands, squeeze the lines laterally between the thumb and forefinger of each hand; then, bending the remaining fingers inwards, exert pressure against both ends. When it is felt that all four sides of the rectangle of type are being subjected to equal pressure, lift from the stick gently, turning the wrists so that the feet of the type point towards you. The weight of the lines will then be resting on the setting-rule, and they may be conveyed with comparative safety to the galley; it is obviously necessary during transit not to relax the pressure of the fingers. To the beginner this operation must seem very hazardous and a feat of considerable skill. Skill indeed it requires, but a reasonable amount of practice will bring confidence and assurance. First attempts in lifting type from the stick should be confined to two or three lines. After more experience full sticks of six or seven lines may be tried.

After type has been set in lines in the stick it is transferred to a galley, where all subsequent operations are conducted until the page is ready to be locked up in a chase for the

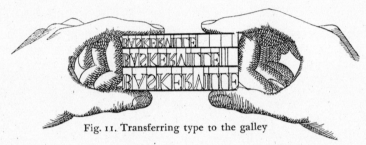

Fig. 11. Transferring type to the galley

printing machine. The galley rests on the sloping work-top of the frame with the closed end to the right and the open end pointing to the left. Lines are deposited on the galley so that the first line of type comes next the closed-in end of the galley. Since the galley is inclined and the type is supported along the length of the top and bottom lines with the setting-rule and lead, there is little chance of a "pie"; but before

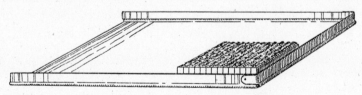

Fig. 12. A page of type on the galley

further work is carried out the lines must be moved along until they make contact with the right angle formed by the lower side and head of the galley. The lines remain in this position while the setting of the next stickful is being completed. It may be necessary to set several stickfuls of type before all the matter is assembled on the galley and "make-up" can begin.

At this point a proof can be taken and given to the reader. This can be effected as described on p. 39, after the type has been safely wedged on the galley with furniture and quoins. A proof is essential so that all corrections to spelling or spacing can be carried out before printing. It is indeed rare to find in any printing-office a page which is free from small errors. A proof which is heavily marked for corrections is known in the printing trade as a "dirty" proof, and its converse is known as a "clean" proof. A proof need not be a perfect impression, but all the letters should show up sufficiently clearly for the proof-reader to carry out his duties. A simple, home-made proofing device, as illustrated on page 39, will serve the purpose admirably.

The term "make-up" covers a multitude of minor operations. The commonest of these is the insertion of leads between lines of type so as to space out the lines in pursuance of a predetermined scheme. In books and pamphlets spaces have to be introduced between the main body of the text and chapter headings or page numbers; in invitation cards and announcements some lines of type must be separated from the others in order to make them stand out clearly. All such arrangements of interlinear spacing are done on the galley by introducing leads of varying thickness between the lines. Any number of leads can be combined together to give different spacing. Should there be only 2-point leads in an equipment and spacing equivalent to 4 points is required, then two leads will be used. Where lines are to be widely separated, as for example, by 12 points, then it is preferable to set a line of quads.

"Make-up" also embraces the insertion of initial letters, ornament or illustration. Wood or linoleum blocks have to be inserted in position and packed out to the correct measure. All blocks require careful justification to the measure of the type, and should have a lead or at least a piece of card at top and bottom to provide an even surface for the type.

After a setting of type has been made up it is made secure by tying it up with string; a strong, fine string is used, and it is better to buy that known as page-cord specially made for

printers. Beginning at the top left-hand corner, one end of
the string is caught and then made fast by the subsequent
laps. The string is lapped round about four or five times, and
the free end is pushed through between the type and the lapped

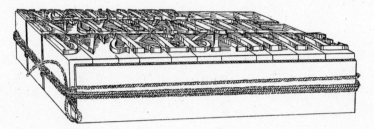

Fig. 13. A page tied up with page-cord

strands to form a small loop. It will be noticed that no knot
is tied, but by a pull on the loop the string can be unfastened
easily. Naturally, the string must be bound round the type
as firmly as possible, and if it is tightened as it laps round
each corner it should grip firmly enough. There must always
be a lead cut to the exact measure at the head and foot of
the page to give it stability.

The tied-up page must be proofed once more to check the
accuracy of the make-up. If a proof is heavily corrected the
page must be untied and the lines that require alteration put
back into the stick for re-setting and re-justification. Good
justification cannot be maintained if lines are corrected on the
galley.

Giving effect to the proof-reader's markings is excellent
practice for reading type. Type is read upside down, beginning
with the first line and reading from left to right. The type
should be read as it is being composed in the stick, and any
errors found must be put right immediately. A second reading
of the type can be made as the page is being made up on the
galley, and a third reading will, of course, be made after a
proof has been pulled. Every opportunity should be taken to
get accustomed to reading type from the "metal." There will
be little difficulty in recognising most letters, but there are

six which are bound to cause considerable confusion. These
letters are b, d, p, q, n, u; when read on the metal they appear as:

p q b d u n

when printed:

b d p q n u

There is really no alternative but to study the form of these
letters very carefully on the types and practise setting words
which contain two or more of them. Beware of turning o, s,
n, u upside down. Distinguish o from figure o, and in case of
small capitals watch for the extra nick on c, i, o, s, v, w,
x, z, made to distinguish them from the lower-case letters
and figures.

CHAPTER 5

COMPOSITION (*continued*)

A good printer is always accurate. Accuracy in setting type includes both justification and the absence of errors in spelling and punctuation. A page of type cannot be considered fit for the printing-machine until proofs have been taken and carefully read over. It should be made a rule that all corrections are made before locking up in the chase. In ordinary printing-offices special presses are employed for proofing, but on account

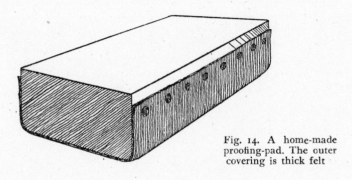

Fig. 14. A home-made proofing-pad. The outer covering is thick felt

of their cost they will not always be available for amateur work. Those who use an Albion press can pull their proofs on it. Those who use a platen press can make an extempore proofing device quite easily. The under side of a piece of thick hardwood is covered with felt or rubber, and two or three sheets of soft paper are placed over the felt to give greater resilience. This home-made press may be called a proofing pad. Proofs are made when the type is in the galley. Galley and type are placed on the imposing surface, and the type, without being removed from the galley, is inked with a hand roller. The roller, or brayer, as it is sometimes called, should have a rather soft composition, and ink must never be allowed to dry on it so that it becomes hard.

When the type has been inked a sheet of soft paper should be laid over it, and the pad, covered side down, should be lowered

very gently on to the paper. The pad is tapped in the centre
with the handle of a mallet. Remember to *tap* and not to
strike the pad; if too much force is used there is a serious
danger of battering the face of the type. The proof is handed
to a reader whose work it is to detect errors of spelling and
faulty spacing. When the corrections indicated by the reader
have been made a further proof is submitted and the process
repeated until a clean sheet is obtained. It is all too easy, when
inking type by hand, to throw the type off its feet so that an
illegible proof is the result. Such an accident can be avoided
if the type is rolled several times from head to foot and *vice-
versa*. Type, when merely tied up, should never be inked from
side to side. Sharpness of impression will be enhanced if too
much ink is not used; a modest amount of ink, evenly distributed
over the roller, produces clear proofs.

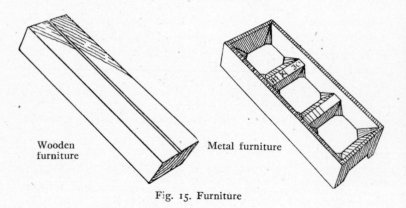

Wooden
furniture

Metal furniture

Fig. 15. Furniture

A page of type which has successfully run the gauntlet of
the reader's watchfulness is ready for imposition. Imposition
is the placing of the type in the right position within a chase
and locking it up securely so that the whole may be lifted, as
a unit, on to the bed of the printing machine.

The galley is placed on the imposing-surface and the type
is removed by sliding it off the open end of the galley. An empty
chase is placed over the page and the forme is "dressed." To
dress a forme is to put pieces of wood and metal furniture in
the space between the sides of the type and the chase. As the

furniture is around all four sides of the type, precautionary measures must be taken to avoid one piece "binding" against another. This danger is overcome by having the furniture on the longer sides of the page overlapping the type by at least half an inch, whilst the furniture on the short sides is shorter than the measure of the type by about one em. When the furniture has been assembled, the page-cord is unwound and removed entirely. Wedges or quoins, by means of which pressure is exerted, are placed in position. The number of quoins needed to lock up a forme depends on the size and nature of the work, but in simple formes with which we are likely to deal two quoins on the long side and one on the short side are all that are required. Quoins are placed close to the inner sides of the chase, and on either side there must be a wooden reglet for them to bite on.

The surface of the type has to be levelled by planing before the quoins are tightened fully. A planer is a flat piece of hardwood, measuring about 6 in. × 4 in., similar to the proofing-pad, but not covered with felt. One side of the planer is perfectly smooth and is known as the face. Its smooth surface must be carefully preserved, and it must never be turned face downwards on the imposing surface; it may pick up small scraps of metal. Planing is done in the same manner as proofing. Little force is required, and the mallet must meet the planer squarely so that it is not dragged over the surface of the type. After each tap the planer is lifted just clear of the type. When the forme has been planed the quoins (either wooden or Hempel) are tightened up, wooden quoins with a shooting-stick and mallet, and metal quoins with the key provided. For a description of the shooting-stick see page 128. No one quoin should be tightened up completely before the others; a few turns or taps should be given to each in succession to ensure pressure being even over the whole forme. The correct position for the type within the chase is a central one.

If type were not put back in the case after it had been printed, a constant supply of new type would be required. It must therefore be distributed. The skill required for distributing type is little less than that required for setting it. A knowledge of the lay of the case is, of course, essential. Type for distribution is placed on a galley, and the ink thoroughly cleaned off with petrol and a pick brush, and the type thoroughly damped to hold it together by capillary attraction. Three or four lines are lifted up as previously described and held in the left hand, as shown in Figure 16. A lead must be placed under the bottom line to prevent collapse. The type is picked up, word by word, with the first finger and thumb of the right hand. The word is read as it is being taken up, and each letter is edged forward by the second and first finger and dropped into the correct compartment of the case. After long practice the sequence of the letters picked up will be memorised, and the whole word can be distributed with considerable celerity. It is best to start, however, by looking at each letter separately before dropping it into its compartment. Very long words should not be picked up whole, but should be divided as con-

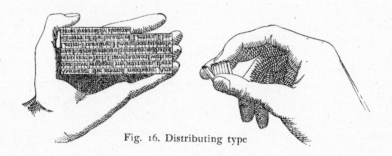

Fig. 16. Distributing type

venience and ease of handling suggest. When distributing settings having small capitals, keep a weather eye open for the extra nicks on c, i, o, s, v, w, x, z. Although distribution may not seem so interesting as composition, yet it must be carried out conscientiously and thoroughly. Careless work would soon throw the type cases into confusion. Type sizes must not be mixed, and if more than one type face is used they must be carefully distinguished.

Printers and authors employ a series of recognised symbols for indicating corrections on proofs. They are unequivocal and express succinctly exactly what is desired. Proofs should have liberal margins in which the corrections can be noted. The list on the opposite page of signs and marks used by proof-readers should be studied.

Zeal to detect errors of spelling and punctuation may be so strong as to allow the question of broken letters to be disregarded. Broken letters are those which, having suffered material damage in some way, no longer have their "face" or printing surface intact. Italic founts are more prone to breakage than roman, particularly the kerned letters such as the lower-case *f* or *y*. It is hardly possible for faults on the face to be recognised when type is being distributed; they can only be detected with certainty on the proof. Readers must therefore be alert to mark damaged letters and, when they are found, the compositor must be prevented from putting them back in the case and so perpetuating the evil.

Proof-readers will find Fowler's *Dictionary of Modern English Usage* (Clarendon Press) a capital guide on difficult points of spelling, punctuation, capitalisation and grammar, while the *Authors' and Printers' Dictionary*, by F. Howard Collins (Humphrey Milford), is to be found in every professional printing office.

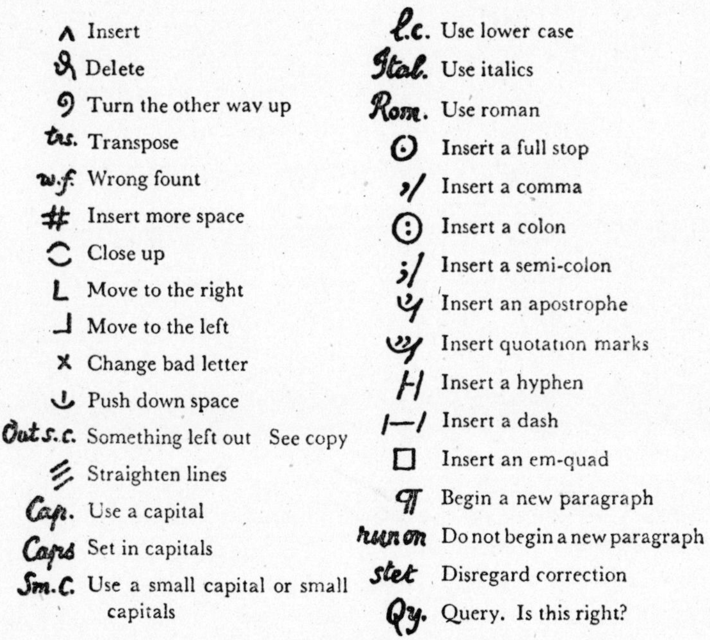

∧ Insert	*l.c.* Use lower case
ℛ Delete	*Ital.* Use italics
↻ Turn the other way up	*Rom.* Use roman
trs. Transpose	⊙ Insert a full stop
w.f. Wrong fount	�ʼ/ Insert a comma
# Insert more space	⊙ Insert a colon
⊂ Close up	;/ Insert a semi-colon
L Move to the right	⸜ Insert an apostrophe
⅃ Move to the left	⸜⸝ Insert quotation marks
✗ Change bad letter	H Insert a hyphen
↧ Push down space	⊢—⊣ Insert a dash
Out s.c. Something left out See copy	☐ Insert an em-quad
⸘ Straighten lines	¶ Begin a new paragraph
Cap. Use a capital	*run on* Do not begin a new paragraph
Caps Set in capitals	*stet* Disregard correction
Sm.c. Use a small capital or small capitals	*Qy.* Query. Is this right?

Fig. 17. Proof-reader's marks

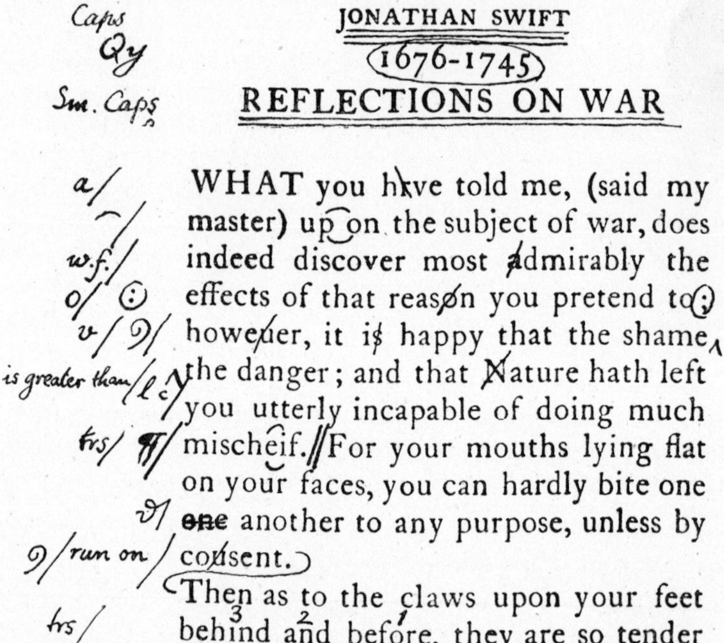

Caps
Qy
Sm. Caps

JONATHAN SWIFT
(1676-1745)
REFLECTIONS ON WAR

a/

w.f./

o/ ⊙

v/ 9/

is greater than/ l c/

trs/ ¶/

9/ run on/

trs/

rom./

#//H/

x/

staun/ Stet

ital/

Out s.c./

g/

WHAT you have told me, (said my
master) up on the subject of war, does
indeed discover most admirably the
effects of that reason you pretend to :
however, it is happy that the shame
the danger; and that Nature hath left
you utterly incapable of doing much
mischeif. For your mouths lying flat
on your faces, you can hardly bite one
one another to any purpose, unless by
consent.
Then as to the claws upon your feet
behind and before, they are so tender
that one of our Yahoos would drive a
dozen of yours before him. And there
fore in recounting the numbers of those
who have been killed in battle, I cannot but think that you have said *the
thing that is not.*
I could not forbear smiling a little at
his ignorance. And being no stranger
to the art of war, I gave a description

N. B. General alignment bad

Fig. 18. A page marked for correction

JONATHAN SWIFT
1667–1745
REFLECTIONS ON WAR

WHAT you have told me, (said my master) upon the subject of war, does indeed discover most admirably the effects of that reason you pretend to : however, it is happy that the shame is greater than the danger ; and that nature hath left you utterly incapable of doing much mischief.

For your mouths lying flat on your faces, you can hardly bite one another to any purpose, unless by consent. Then as to the claws upon your feet before and behind, they are so tender that one of our Yahoos would drive a dozen of yours before him. And therefore in recounting the numbers of those who have been killed in battle, I cannot but think that you have *said the thing that is not*.

I could not forbear shaking my head and smiling a little at his ignorance. And being no stranger to the art of war, I gave a description of cannons, cul-

Fig. 19. The same page corrected

D

CHAPTER 6

PLATEN PRESSWORK

In both professional and amateur printing offices small formes are printed on a type of press known as a platen-press. The mechanical principle of this kind of press involves the bringing of a level plate firmly up against a rigid bed on which the chase containing the forme has been secured. A sheet of paper is placed on the movable plate, or "platen," and is brought into contact with the face of the type, causing an impression to be made.

A craftsman must always understand the tools with which he works, and the printing-press is no exception. It is very desirable to have a grasp of the construction and main parts of the platen-press. Built into the cast-iron frame, towards the back, is the "bed" (c—refer to Figure 20 on opposite page) on which the type-forme rests. The type is, of course, locked up in a chase when it comes from the imposing-surface, and therefore can be lifted with perfect safety on to the bed of the machine. The chase is held fast by two fixed clips at the bottom of the bed and a spring clip at the top. On either side of the bed are vertical tracks for the bearings on the two rollers (B). As they run up and down the tracks the bearings revolve, and since they fit tightly on the roller-spindle, the whole roller is kept turning constantly, thus spreading the ink evenly. Above the bed is a rotating steel disc (D) from which the rollers draw their supply of ink. The disc rotates in order to facilitate the even distribution of the ink. After passing over the disc, the rollers run down the tracks and come into contact with the face of the type, depositing on it a film of ink. When the rollers have reached the lowest point of their travel they return over the forme to the rotating disc for the purpose of replenishing their supply of ink.

After the type has been inked the impression is made by the platen, carrying the paper towards the bed of the press. In actual practice the platen does not touch the bed; the type intervenes and receives the force of the impression. A toggle-

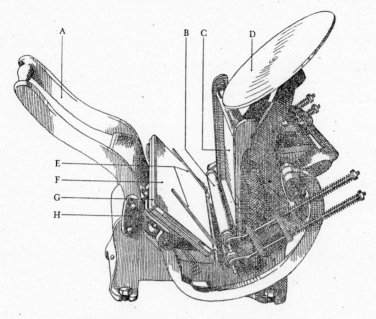

A. Impression lever   E. Friskets
B. Inking roller   F. Platen
C. Bed.   G. Platen clamp
D. Ink distributor   H. Toggle

Fig. 20. A small platen-press

motion (H), actuated by a hand lever (A) or else a treadle, is normally employed to move the platen (F) towards the bed. When the platen "opens" away from the bed the rollers automatically move downwards and ink the forme; as the platen closes the rollers move up towards the distributing disc and are clear of both bed and platen before the impression is made.

The paper must be kept in position whilst the platen is moving towards the bed, and it is equally necessary to disengage the paper from the face of the type and carry it back with the platen after the impression. Two vertical metal fingers (E) perform these duties; they are known as the frisket or grippers and are mounted on a bar below the bottom of the platen. Both grippers can be moved independently along the bar. The platen has, along its top and lower edges, clamps (G) for the purpose of holding in tension the "make-ready" sheets; these clamps are readily loosened by leverage from the screw-driver supplied with the press. The strength of the impression of the platen against the face of the type-forme can be varied by fastening more or fewer sheets to the make-ready on the platen.

No one can live long in a printing office without becoming aware of constant references to "make-ready." Make-ready is the preparatory work necessary to obtain an even and clear impression of the type on the paper, and it is carried out on the platen. Some preparatory work must be done before a press is ready to receive a forme. The bed of the machine requires wiping over with an oily rag to remove grit and dirt and to prevent rust; the rollers have to be taken out of their storage box and washed free from dust and grease with petrol and rags. A runner has to be put on either end of each roller-spindle. In order to make the rollers turn, these runners should either fit tightly against the composition or be keyed to the spindle by a peg. The rollers are then put in their respective bearings on the roller-carriage of the machine.

The following practical hints will serve as a guide to a beginner. Take a screw-driver and loosen the two clamps at the top and bottom of the platen, and lay the make-ready sheets under them. The platen has to be covered with a number of sheets which are known as the tympan. To make up the tympan a small supply of the following material, cut to the sizes desired, should be at hand. Strong manilla paper four inches longer than the platen, and one inch less in width; soft writing-paper cut to the full length of the platen, but one inch less in depth; three-sheet boards cut to the same size as the writing-paper and some sheets of tissue paper. Take a sheet of manilla paper and fold it back half an inch from the bottom edge. Lever open the clamp at the foot of the platen and insert the folded edge of double thickness under the clamp at the bottom; then close down the clamp. The sheet should be fixed in a central position so that it leaves a margin of about half an inch on each side of the platen. Then lay a three-sheet board on the platen, beneath the manilla, and on top of this place two sheets of the soft writing-paper. Insert the manilla or "draw-sheet" under the *top* clamp. Holding the draw-sheet with the left hand stroke it up from the bottom of the platen with the right hand. When the sheets are perfectly taut, close down the top clamp. Tear off any ragged edges of paper which may be left beyond the clamp.

Now, with a palette knife, spread a small portion of ink, as evenly as possible, on the revolving disc; one or two streaks across the surface should be sufficient. Run the machine until the ink appears to be well distributed, finally bringing it to rest with the rollers at the bottom limit of their travel. The press is now ready for the chase. Hold the chase by the two top corners,

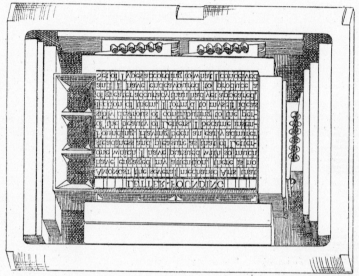

Fig. 21. A forme correctly locked up in chase for a platen press

and lower it gently between the roller-tracks at the side of the bed; when it has reached the bottom clips, the clip at the top of the bed is lifted up and allowed to spring back again so as to grip the upper edge of the chase. Care must be taken not to damage the type face when putting the forme into the machine. It should be observed that all type is locked up in the centre of the chase, and the head of the type matter should be nearest the floor with the quoins towards the top and right-hand side.

It is important to see that the frisket fingers do not foul the type in the chase. Using the spanner provided, loosen the nuts and slide the friskets along the bar until they are clear of the type and fall opposite the margins.

Take a sheet of the soft writing-paper, lay it on the top of the tympan lightly, sticking the two top corners with paste, and make an impression. An inspection of the printing of this sheet may reveal a general weakness, indicating that more pressure is required, in which case an extra sheet or sheets of manilla paper, cut to size, can be added to the tympan. If, however, the impression is too heavy the tympan must be reduced.

Having adjusted the tympan to give the desired general pressure, take another impression as before on a fresh loose sheet of paper. On examination it may be found that whilst some of the letters show up clearly there are others which are quite indistinct. These indistinct letters, which are "low," require more pressure. Make an impression on the draw-sheet, and in the places where the letters do not show up strongly paste on small patches of tissue paper. Overlay all weak spots in the impression with tissue until the impression appears to be level in every part of the sheet. Be sparing with paste when patching, for large clots are likely to swell the packing and too strong an impression will result. A thick flour paste has good properties. This paste is made by adding ordinary flour to cold water and boiling in a double kettle, stirring until it attains the required thickness.

It is very clear that successive sheets must be placed on the platen in precisely the same position, so that the impression of the type on the paper will maintain the same relative position throughout any given piece of work. This can be achieved quite

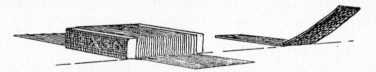

Fig. 22. Position gauges and tags for tympan

easily by fixing two sets of gauges at right angles to one another. Quads glued on to the draw-sheet make admirable gauges. To fix the position for the gauges measure the depth of margin desired from the head of the type to the top of the paper and also from the left side of the type to the left edge of the paper. Plot these two measurements in pencil on the draw-sheet, using, of course. the impression as a key. The two lines will mark where the paper is to be placed on the platen. Fix two quads by means of paste along the line plotted at the foot, and fix an additional quad on the line drawn at the left at right angles to the other. The quads must not be placed indiscriminately in any position on the lines. The correct position for the quads can be ascertained by taking a sheet of the paper which is to be printed and folding it three times, as shown in Figure 23. On the long side of the sheet there will be three creases and on the short side one crease. The first and third creases mark the position for the quads at the foot, and the crease on the short side is the position for the quad at the left. Before the paste

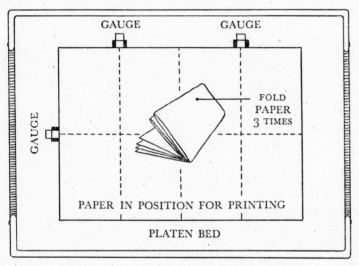

Fig. 23. How to find the position for the gauges

has set firmly feed in a sheet and test if the gauges are correctly set. Make adjustments if necessary, and finally fix the gauges firmly by covering the quads and a small surface of the platen with strips of gummed paper.

Small tags should be placed by the side of the gauges to act as guides when laying on the sheets. They also assist the frisket in pulling the sheets away from the forme after the impression has been taken. To make tags, cut three strips of three-sheet board one inch long by half an inch wide, and paste one half of their length on the draw-sheet close up to the quads, leaving the unpasted half hanging over the margin. Bend up the front loose half slightly so that the sheets can pass freely to the gauges. A little care will have to be taken to prevent them from coming into contact with the type when printing.

The friskets must now be re-adjusted so that they will not foul either the gauges or the type when an impression is taken. From the right-hand side of the tympan pull one of the loose manilla or note-paper sheets gently out from under the draw-sheet and lay it to the gauges on the top of all the other packing. Cut down the size so that it does not come beyond the top edge of the platen, and allow it to come within about two inches from the right-hand side edge. Fix this sheet down firmly by pasting along the top edge and at the two bottom corners. This covering sheet serves to soften the effect of the make-ready and to guard it from damage.

Final preparations can now be made for running off the work. The top sheet must be free of paste and ink so that the paper will not be smudged on the reverse side as it is being printed. The amount of ink requires graduating. An excess of ink must be avoided; too generous a supply will thicken up the face of the type. When adding ink spread it as evenly as possible with the palette knife over the rotating disc and, placing a waste sheet on the platen. take a series of impressions until the ink appears to be well distributed. Examine the top sheet once again to see that it is perfectly clean, and then start to feed the paper into the machine. Place a pile of the paper on a small table on the right-hand side of the machine and fan it out so that successive sheets can be readily picked up. Take up the first sheet with the right hand and place it on the platen so that it touches the two bottom gauges; then push it over to the left until the left side gauge is touched. Pull down the lever. or operate the treadle, and make the impression. When the platen opens the printed sheet is removed with the left hand and placed on a table. It is preferable to work with two tables : one on the right of the printing-machine for the blank paper and the other on the left to receive the printed sheets. Careful handling of the sheets immediately after printing is very desirable. Until the ink has been given time to dry, sheets cannot be subjected to friction or pressure without risk of set-off. Even slight rubbing is sufficient to cause set-off. The term "set-off" is used to describe any marking or smudging that results from ink being transferred from the printed side of a sheet to the underside of the sheet immediately above it. Set-off is a bugbear in all printing offices, and constant care and watchfulness must be exercised to avoid it.

Make-ready for work printed in two colours does not differ materially from work in one colour, except that two formes have to be printed and the rollers and inking disc washed up for the second colour. In two-colour work the "key-forme" is printed first and the second colour is registered to it. An example of two-colour printing is an invitation card with border in red and the type in black. In this instance the border would be the key-forme and is printed first, as it will be easier to fix the margins from the border than from the type within. If, however, the card has no border, then the black would be the key-forme, and the line or lines of red would be printed in register after it.

It is sometimes distressingly hard to get a sharp, clean impression from the type. This can happen even if the make-ready has been done with adequate skill. A slur may be caused if the grippers, or friskets, fail to pull the sheet away from the forme. Sometimes the sheet is peeled off the face of the forme instead of being drawn off evenly. To overcome this trouble more holding-power must be given to the grippers; the application of a binding of sandpaper round the prongs will increase their hold on the paper and enable them to do their work effectively. But it sometimes happens that the size of the paper is insufficient to allow the friskets to get a good grip. A thin elastic band stretched over both friskets will overcome the difficulty, but care has to be taken that it runs along a margin so that there will be no risk of its encountering the type when an impression is taken.

Another cause of slur, or indistinct impression, may be due to unsuitable ink. When printing on Bond and good writing papers a very stiff ink is required, and special "Bond" inks should be used. Antiques and smooth book-papers do not require a stiff ink; an ordinary "half-tone black" gives the best results on this class of paper.

A printing-press will have a long and useful life if it is looked after properly. It must be kept clean and be well oiled. An oil-can is provided with the equipment, and it should be used on all the oil-holes every day when the press is in use. Ink must never be allowed to dry on the rotating disc or on the rollers. After the day's work the inking disc must be thoroughly cleaned with rags and petrol or paraffin. The rollers also must be removed from the press and cleaned in the same way. When they are clean a thin coating of machine-oil is applied. It is preferable to keep rollers in a box with spindles resting on ledges, so that the composition is clear of the bottom. They must never be wrapped in paper. Spare rollers may be kept in flannel. Roller composition is extremely pliable and easily gets "flats" if it rests on any surface. Flats on the circumference of the rollers unfit them for use. Composition rollers are also affected by changes of atmosphere, so they should not be exposed to extremes of temperature.

Rolling the type plays an important part in getting a clean, sharp impression. When the surface of rollers becomes hard or glossy they lose their "tack" and need re-clothing. Rollers in good condition cling slightly when grasped by the hand. When newly cast they should be slightly larger in diameter than the runners. Rollers should be re-coated at least once a year. In damp weather they are likely to absorb moisture and swell and press too heavily on the type, causing the letters to be clogged with ink. To overcome this, some strips of gummed paper stuck along the roller tracks will relieve the pressure. In dry weather the reverse may happen, the rollers shrinking and not inking the type properly. To meet this difficulty, take one or more sheets from under the draw-sheet and paste them on the back of the forme. Keep roller tracks free from grease, so that the runners revolve the rollers as they travel over the type; to allow them to slide down would be fatal to clear printing.

Two strips of metal or wood about half an inch wide and of type height can be locked up with the forme to assist in the revolving of the rollers. These strips, or bearers, are placed in the chase at the extreme right and left sides of the forme. They can only be used when the paper being printed is small enough to come between them. Otherwise, of course, the bearers would print.

After a forme has been printed off, the top clip on the bed is drawn back and the chase removed. Ink must never be allowed to dry on the type, and the machine operator should clean the forme thoroughly with a stiff brush soaked in petrol, drying it with some soft rags.

CHAPTER 7

THE ALBION PRESS

In choosing between a small hand-worked platen and an Albion, we have on the one hand the advantages of the greater speed and mechanical inking of the "platen" and on the other the larger size of the Albion, together with the possibility of doing work of a better quality with it. The small platen-presses, whose reasonable price puts them within the average amateur's reach, are only suitable for light work. A forme of the largest size that their chases will hold tries their strength severely, and it will generally be found impossible to get a sufficiently heavy impression from such formes on a good paper. With careful make-ready and sympathetic paper, decent results can be had from solid pages of type of moderate proportions, but they are much better adapted for printing display settings of an open character such as letter-headings, invitations, announcements, and all those odd jobs that are chiefly demanded from school printers. Those who intend to print small books will inevitably choose the Albion, because of its capacity to print sheets containing several pages and the greater strength of its impression. They will miss the easy working of the platen-press and its automatic inking. With a hand "platen" a speed of 500 impressions to the hour may be reached, while with an Albion 100 will be nearer the mark. It takes a long while to learn to ink with a hand-roller as efficiently as with the mechanically controlled rollers of the platen presses.

On every ground it is desirable for schools to possess both a small platen and an Albion so as to use each for the kind of work to which it is better suited.

The Albion press is an iron version of the old hand-press made of wood, used from the invention of printing until 1800. In addition to the change of material, presses of the Albion class embody a toggle-motion for forcing down the platen instead of the earlier screw. Their introduction was the outcome of many years of experimental work done by Lord Stanhope.

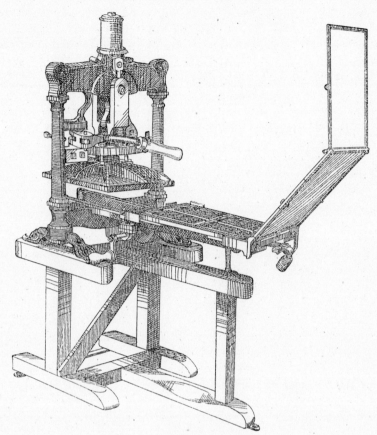

Fig. 24. A small Albion press

In the Albion press the impression is made by a horizontal surface called the platen, actuated by a hand-lever, descending on the forme, lying on another horizontal surface called the bed. The platen is made to rise to its normal position clear of the type by a spring. Since the rise and fall of the platen cannot practically be made more than about half an inch, it is necessary to move the forme from under the platen in order to ink it and to lay on the paper. This is done by making the bed slide backwards and forwards on runners.

For the purpose of taking rough proofs it is sufficient to lay the paper directly on the type, but for printing a run of

work with impressions in exactly the same position on a number
of sheets the press is equipped with tympans. The tympans are
so called because they are made, like kettle-drums, of parchment stretched taut on frames. They serve a double purpose.
Firstly they provide a surface to which the sheets may be
fastened in a certain position in relation to the forme: they
are hinged to one end of the bed so as to fall on the forme and
hold the paper in position above the face of the type during
the running-in of the bed and the taking of the impression.
Secondly they provide a padding to soften the impact of the
platen and make the impression somewhat elastic. For this
second purpose they are made in two parts, the inner and the
outer tympans, that come apart to admit layers of padding
between them.

The structure of an Albion press is best explained by references to a picture. The backbone of it is the staple to which the
moving parts are attached. The staples of large presses fit in
sockets in heavy iron feet standing on the floor. In many small
ones the staple and the feet are cast in one piece, and the whole
is screwed on a wooden trestle. The vertical parts of the staple
are called pillars and the horizontal member that joins them at
the top is known as the head. The transverse bar lower down
is the winter that supports the bed when it is run in under the
platen. The platen itself is suspended from the head of the
staple by means of the piston and is attached to it by four
detachable platen-screws that fit sockets in the platen and pass
through a flange round the lower end of the piston. By means
of the nuts on these screws the platen can be adjusted to a
horizontal position. The piston slides up and down. It is held
in its normal raised position by a strong spiral spring enclosed
in the cap resting on top of the head. A metal loop hangs
from the spring and connects it with the piston by means of
a steel bolt, the "spring bolt," passing through the head and the
piston and the eye in the loop. The holes in the head through
which it goes are oval to allow it to move up and down. The
toggle-motion that forces the piston (and with it the platen)
downwards fits inside the piston. It consists of two parts, the
chill and the fulcrum. When the fulcrum stands upright it
holds the piston at the bottom of its stroke, and this causes the
impression. The upper end of the fulcrum bears on the chill

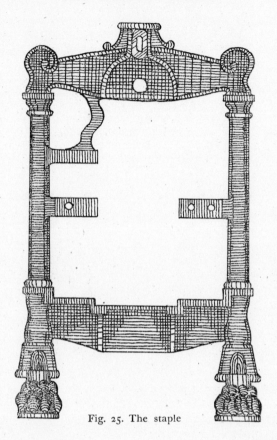

Fig. 25. The staple

and forces it upwards against the head of the staple. The lower end of the fulcrum bears on flanges inside the piston and forces it down on the platen. When the piston rises to the top of its stroke the fulcrum assumes a slanting position. To allow the fulcrum to stand either upright or slanting there is a triangular opening in the chill. The chill is pivoted near the top about a steel bolt (the "main bolt") that passes through it and the head of the staple. This bolt passes the thrust from the toggle-motion on to the staple. The main bolt has also to pass through the piston: in order that the piston may move up and down in relation to the staple and the chill, the holes in it to admit the main bolt are elongated vertically to the length of the stroke.

The bed of the press, on which the forme lies, is a steel casting perfectly flat on top and with two long flanges underneath made to fit grooves in the two runners called ribs that support the bed and provide a track on which it can run backwards and forwards.

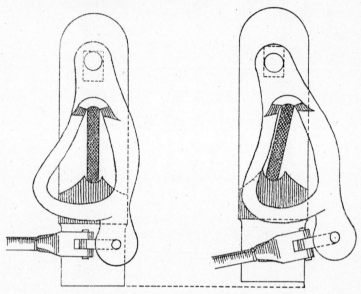

Fig. 26. The piston and toggle-motion of an Albion press

One end of the ribs is supported by the winter (the transverse member of the staple that joins the two pillars near the feet of the press), and the other end, furthest from the staple, is carried by an upright called the fore-foot. The bed is made to move along the ribs by means of a little winch called the rounce. At either end of the bed is a clamp that screws up and grips one end of a strip of webbing material. The other end of each of the strips, or girths as they are technically called, is nailed to the wooden barrel of the rounce, in such a way that the bed can be hauled in or out by turning the handle of the rounce one way or other.

The bed itself has raised corner-pieces to act as bearings for wedges that hold the chase laid on the bed firmly in position and two hinges at the end furthest from the staple by means of which the tympans are fastened to it.

The tympans are two steel frames, one fitting inside another, with a covering of parchment or bookbinder's cloth stretched across them. The smaller one, called the inner tympan, is a simple rectangle; it is laid inside the outer tympan and kept there by swivelling hooks on top of the outer tympan engaging studs on the other.

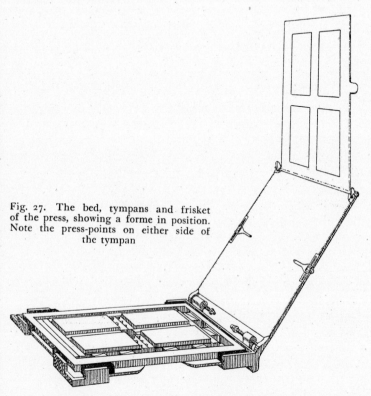

Fig. 27. The bed, tympans and frisket of the press, showing a forme in position. Note the press-points on either side of the tympan

The outer tympan is more complicated than the other. At its lower end it has hinges fitting those of the bed, and at the other, smaller hinges for attaching the frisket. The hinges for the frisket should project so far that when the tympan falls on the bed they hold it as far off the bed at one end as the hinges connecting the tympan and bed do at the other. (Frequently one finds extempore frisket-joints on a press that do not jut out enough, allowing the top end of the tympans to rest on the type, causing slurred impressions.)

E

Half-way along either side of the outer tympan is a slot made to admit screws for holding attachments called points that have little spikes that pierce the paper at each impression and provide a means for positioning the sheets when they come to be printed on the other side.

The frisket is a very light steel frame, easily detachable from the tympan. At the near side it has a projecting thumb-piece, made to clear the point-screws, serving as a handle for raising and lowering the tympans before and after the impression. In use the frisket is covered like the tympans with a piece of strong paper. The area to be printed is cut out of the covering, leaving a network between and round the pages. Its function is partly to hold the sheet that is to be printed flat on the tympan and partly to protect the margins of the sheets from being smeared with stray ink lying on the furniture in the forme.

The platen is pulled down towards the bed by means of a handle called the bar that turns about a pin going through it into sockets projecting from the near-side pillar of the staple. The bar describes a quarter of a circle when it is pulled over, and, through a coupling-bar joining it to the chill, actuates the toggle-motion inside the piston. The spring over the head of the press in raising the piston also pulls the bar back to its normal position lying across the staple of the press.

Every printer should know how to erect his press. In this section it is assumed that the press is of folio size. A larger one had better be erected by a professional, since the work might be not only arduous but dangerous.

The first thing is to lift the staple into the position where it is finally to stand. When the press is assembled it will be difficult to move it. To get the right light the staple should be near a window or, better still, between two windows, so that the light falls on the tympans when they are raised. The staple should therefore be nearer the window than the tympans. For night work there should be a light directly over the bed of the press when it is rolled out from under the platen.

When the staple is in position, put the cap with the spring in it into its socket on top of the head. Then raise the piston from underneath so that it fits on either side of the head. Push the thinner of the two steel bolts through the topmost holes in the piston and the head of the staple and the steel loop hanging from the spring. This hangs the piston up. Fit the cheeks into the notches on either side of the flange at the lower end of the piston, and screw them on to the corresponding projections from the pillars of the staple. Attach the coupling-bar to the chill by putting their steel pin in from the top. Then insert the chill, with the coupling-bar going first, from the off side into the piston; and, tilting the chill so that the hollow opening in it is clear of the piston on the off side, put the fulcrum inside this opening. Get the bottom of the fulcrum into the sockets in the flanges inside the piston. Then raise the chill to an upright position and push the main bolt with one of its steel washers on it from back to front through the lower holes in the piston, and the head of the staple and the hole at the top of the chill. Put the other washer on the end of the bolt and drop in the cotter-pin through the little hole in the end of the bolt. Drop the four platen-screws into the holes in the top of the platen and put in the iron keys that hold them in place. One person raises the platen so that the screws go through the holes made for them at the lower end of the piston, while another fits the nuts on the tips of the screws projecting above the flange on the piston. In some presses there are nuts on the screws to fit above and below the flange on the piston. By adjusting these conjointly the platen can be held rigidly at any desired distance from the piston. In others there are nuts above the flange on the piston only; with this arrangement there must be some packing put between the lower end of the piston and the top of the platen. The thickness of this packing can be varied to give the required amount of pressure. A small block of iron is generally used, its thickness varying with every press. The packing can be put in when the press is completely assembled by loosening the platen-screws. At this point wind up the spring at the top as far as possible by turning the nut above it inside the cap; this raises the piston.

Having temporarily hung the platen, you must attach the ribs to the winter. This is usually done by a bolt with a nut on the end passing through a cross-piece, joining the two ribs and a plate of steel, which is forced by the nut against the under sides of flanges on the winter. There is an attachment behind and in front of the winter. This device, and not a rigid joint, is used so that the ribs may be moved slightly from side to side if it is desired to make the tympans project over the bed on one side or other without hitting against the staple. The projecting end of the ribs is fixed by means of the fore-foot so that they are at right angles to the staple. The bed is now laid on the ribs, and a girth is clamped to either end. Assuming that the rounce is ready fitted in its bearings under the ribs, the next step is to attach the loose ends of the girths to the wooden barrel of the rounce. The clamps attaching the girths to the bed are not central; accordingly, as the clamp is nearer the near or the off side, the girth must be fastened on the near or off side of the barrel. Push the bed as far in as it will go, and nail the end of the girth attached to the far end to the barrel of the rounce so that it is taut. Use two short flat-headed tacks that can easily be levered out by the head when the girth is taken off. Then wind the rounce and pull the bed out to the fullest extent (see that the nailed girth is tightly wound), and then nail the end of the other girth so that it is taut. Any subsequent adjustments can be made by means of the clamps on the bed. The girths should be doubled over where they pass through the clamps.

The bar should now be fitted. It is attached to the staple by a steel pin going through two sockets projecting inwards from the near-side pillar. Before joining the coupling-bar to the bar you must relax the spring at the top of the press. Then the coupling-bar can be joined to the bar by means of a steel pin passing through holes in both.

The press is now completely assembled. Nevertheless, a good deal more remains to be done before it is fit for work.

All the moving parts of the press must be kept well oiled. It makes presswork much easier to keep plenty of oil in the ribs, so that the bed runs in and out easily.

The tympans have to be covered with parchment. Cover the inner tympan first, since it is smaller and less complicated. Rub the parchment well with a wet sponge on both sides and lay it on a flat surface. Coat the frame of the tympan heavily with flour-and-water paste, and put paste round the edges of the parchment also. Lay the frame squarely on the parchment and cut the latter round the frame, leaving a margin of an inch and a half all round. Cut the corners off obliquely and cut notches for the hinges, studs, and similar projections from the frames.

Then wrap the edges of the parchment round the frames, getting it even and quite tight all over, and finally tucking the edges in. When the parchment dries it should be taut and rigid as a drum.

The parchment on both tympans should be on the under side of the frames, so that it comes between them and the bed. In covering the outer tympan leave the slots for the point-screws clear. Unless the parchment is taut the impression will be apt to slur.

Put a piece of linen folded in four between the tympans and cut it to the exact size. On top of it put a sheet of card-board large enough to fit the tympans.

Before trying the effect of a pull from type it is prudent to adjust the platen so that it hangs level. Raise the tympans and run the bed in. Take a block of wood and mark the height of one corner of the platen from the bed; then test the other three corners. By turning the nuts on the platen-screws the platen can be made to hang parallel with the bed.

Now put a large forme on the bed and try a pull from it. Probably the impression will be much too weak and also heavier at one corner than the other. Put sheets of paper in the tympans to make the impression heavy enough, and go on adjusting the platen-screws until all four corners of the platen bear equally strongly on the type. If it is not possible to get a sufficiently heavy impression with three or four sheets of thin paper in the tympans, more packing must be put between the piston and the platen. The less padding there is in the tympans the sharper will be the impression. Amateurs often make the mistake of putting far too much in the tympans so that the impression goes too deeply into the paper, making the back of the sheet look heavily embossed. When the impression is right, the back of the sheet will be only just perceptibly dented and yet the ink will have been pressed into the paper so that it cannot all be rubbed away with the finger-tip. Connoisseurs adapt the force of the impression to the different things that they print. Some types look best lightly impressed; others, Caslon among them, benefit by a somewhat heavy impression.

The largest chase that can properly be used in a press is one measuring an inch less than the bed, both lengthwise and in breadth. This leaves room for quoins fastening it in position

and allows for adjustments of the quoins to get register on the
two sides of the sheet. The best chases are made of steel or
wrought iron. Cast-iron ones are considerably cheaper, and in
folio size are quite satisfactory; their worst feature being that
the extra thickness cuts down the space available for the type.
Whatever be the kind of chases selected, they should be bought
in pairs corresponding exactly with one another. If the chases
used for two formes to be printed back-to-back are dissimilar,
the business of making register will be troublesome.

CHAPTER 8

IMPOSING FOR THE ALBION PRESS

In our previous directions for imposition we gave instructions for locking up small formes, consisting of only one page, for the platen-press. The Albion press being bigger will often be used to print sheets consisting of several pages. This makes imposition much more difficult and fuller directions may be found useful.

Having the pages ready tied up on galleys, the compositor must refer to an imposition-scheme and slide the pages needed for his forme from the galley on to the "stone" or imposing-surface.

Imposition-schemes for formes containing two, four, six, and eight pages are given here. For the Albion press the scheme should be arranged, as these are, so that the sheet is turned from end to end to print the second side. Otherwise, if the type is far out of the centre of the chase, it may prove impossible to shift the forme sideways far enough to make the two sides register.

These schemes indicate the arrangement of pages for the first section of a book. In the subsequent sections the pages will come in the same order; in the case of an octavo, page 17 in the second section will come in the same position as page 1 in the first and the others in sequence. A table with sixteen columns should be drawn up showing which pages take the place of pages 1 to 16 in subsequent sections.

The names folio, quarto, octavo, etc., are commonly used of impositions for a full sheet. In printing with a folio-sized press, however, the sheet will be half-size, so that an imposition of eight pages to the forme will result in pages half the size of an octavo in the ordinary sense of the term. It will be less confusing to avoid speaking of impositions in quarto, octavo, etc., and use the expressions "in twos," "in fours," "in sixes," and so on. These are applied to arrangements of two, four, and six pages to the forme respectively. Since there are two formes to every sheet (one for each side), each scheme of imposition gives a sheet of twice as many pages.

In the case of a folio-sized press it must be remembered that sheets of quarto pages—the largest that can be printed if the work is to be bound in book form—will have to be quired to give good results in the binding. One thickness is not enough for the sewing unless the paper is very good. This fact makes it necessary to set eight quarto pages at a time. Impositions giving four or eight pages to the forme will be the most useful. Occasionally a sheet of twelve square pages may be found suitable for a piece of work. The plans given here show the positions for the pages in the two formes needed for both sides of a sheet.

When the completed job will consist of many sheets folded and bound, the first page of every sheet should bear a distinguishing mark at the foot to serve as a quick guide to the binder as to the order in which to collate the sheets. These marks, called signatures, are letters or figures set below the foot of the page.

The printer can easily draw up a scheme for himself if an out-of-the-way imposition is called for. He has only to fold a sheet, number its pages, and lay it face down on another flat sheet, on which he can mark the positions of the pages as they will come in the forme.

When the pages of a forme have been laid down in the right positions the next step is to put strips of furniture between them to make the margins of the proper width.

The most satisfactory way of fixing margins for beginners is to fold a sheet into pages and get the layout-man to draw the type area (exact size) on the outside page. Make pinpricks at the four corners so as to show the corners of the printed area on every page in the sheet, and draw pencil lines connecting them. This gives a diagram showing the right spacing between the pages. The distance between every two pages should be measured, and furniture, reglets and leads totalling this amount put between the pages in the forme.

Avoid having long strips of furniture between pages going from end to end of the forme. It is well to provide for the pages varying slightly in size: and, if there is one long piece of furniture abutting on several pages that are not identical in size, it will bear harder on some pages than on others when

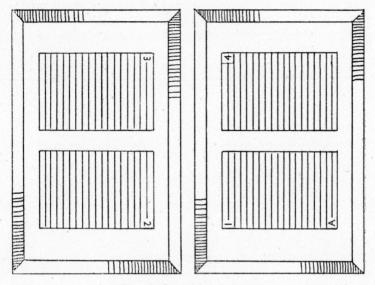

Fig. 28. Imposition in twos

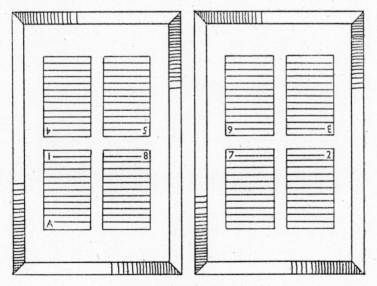

Fig. 29. Imposition in fours

Fig. 30. Imposition in twos quired

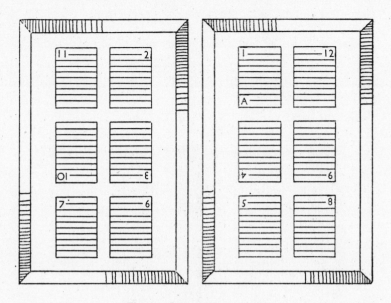

Fig. 31. Imposition in sixes

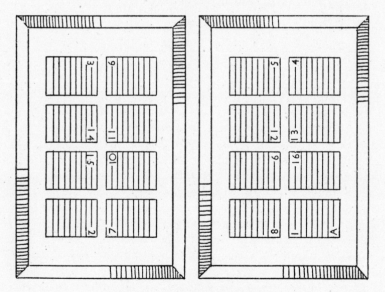

Fig. 32. Imposition in eights

the forme is locked up. Therefore it is best to use short pieces of furniture that will exert pressure on one page only. It is an advantage to have a lead or two as well as wooden furniture between pages, because leads are easily taken out in case it is found necessary to decrease a margin to make register between two sides of a sheet.

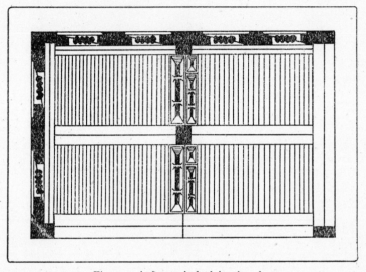

Fig. 33. A forme locked in the chase

Very great care must be taken to prevent furniture meeting at the corners of pages in such a way that, when the quoins are tightened, the pressure is prevented from being exerted on the type. If furniture "binds" in this way the type will fall out of the forme when the chase is lifted, a menace so serious as to make the compositor very careful to see that there are intervals at all angles where furniture meets.

Supposing that the pages are by this time all separated by furniture, it remains to surround the outside of the forme with material for wedging it tight in the chase. Put the chase on the stone round the pages. As far as possible arrange furniture round the forme so as to get the type centred in the chase. Put long strips along one side and at one end of the forme. The quoins will go on the other side and at the other end. It is advisable, in view of possible differences in the lengths of the pages, not to have the quoins at the side all bearing on one long piece of furniture. In a chase of folio size it will be better to have two separate lengths, each with a pair of quoins acting on it and each abutting on one or two pages. The furniture at the side, called side-sticks, should be at least 36 points wide.

Metal quoins should never touch the chase: reglets or pieces of cardboard should be put between the two.

Whether the quoins are wooden or metal they should be so arranged that the act of tightening them makes them slide away from the quoins at right angles with them. Otherwise they will squeeze the forme out of square as they are tightened. In the case of wooden quoins and tapering sidesticks, this means that the thin ends of the sticks at the foot and the side meet one another at the corner. In the case of metal quoins the far side must slide away from the quoins at right-angles with them.

When the forme is dressed the quoins should be tightened with the fingers and the type levelled with a planer and mallet. This must be done thoroughly and deliberately, but undue violence shortens the life of the type.

Locking up, or driving the quoins, is begun at the end. When the end is half-tightened, the side is also tightened slightly. Thus the pressure from the end and the side is increased alternately until the forme is rigid.

To test the effect of locking-up, raise a corner of the forme slightly and try pushing the type down with the thumb. Try the pages all over in this way, to detect "binds" of furniture or leads and short lines or short pages.

When the forme is rigid enough to resist thumb-pressure all over, it is ready for press.

CHAPTER 9

PRINTING WITH THE ALBION PRESS

After wiping the bed quite clean, lay the forme on it. If the chase is nearly as large as the bed will allow, it should be fastened in position by means of wooden wedges, called quoins, wedged between the outside of the chase and the raised corners of the bed. Whatever may be the size of the chase, it must be firmly wedged into the bed so that the roller and the jarring of the carriage will not cause it to shift during the run. It must also be fixed so that it can easily be moved slightly in all four directions. The chase should be put exactly in the centre of the bed. This point is shown by the intersection of two lines crossing the bed, engraved in the surface. If it is off centre it will tend to tilt the platen out of the horizontal and strain the platen-screws. A small chase may be wedged in position by means of empty chases, blocks of wood, or anything else that is handy. A way of fixing medium-sized formes is shown in Figure 36.

Very much better results will be got from small formes if they have type-high bearers at the corners to take the weight of the platen. Formes that have much more type at one end than another print too black at the end where there is more white space, unless there are bearers there to take the weight of the platen. Bearers are indispensable to good work.

Having fastened the forme in the press, half-loosen the quoins inside, plane the forme down carefully by tapping the face of the type with a planer and mallet, and then lock it up again.

It is now time to ink the forme and take a proof to make sure that no letters have fallen out during imposition. For proofing it is sufficient to lay the paper on the type.

When the proof has been scrutinised, proceed to find the right position on the tympan for laying on the sheets. Fasten a sheet of thin paper to the tympan, so big as to cover the whole of it, with dabs of paste at the four corners and half-way down the sides. An impression, with ink, should be taken on this when it is fixed. Using the impression as a guide, the correct margins all the way round the sheet should be tentatively marked in pencil. The outline will show the position in which sheets are to be laid on the tympan.

If the work to be printed is not afterwards to be folded into pages, the sheets will simply be laid against guides made of bent pins pushed sideways into the parchment of the tympan, provided the sheet has two straight trimmed edges to lay against the guides. Two pins at the side, and one at the bottom, will be enough. Those at the side should be as far apart as possible.

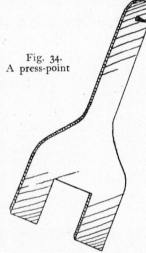

Fig. 34.
A press-point

When the forme is of several pages and the sheets of paper have uneven edges the best way of making register is to use press-points. They must be adjusted on the tympan so that they come in the line of the fold half-way down the sheet. The centre of the margin where the fold will be should be drawn in pencil on the sheet of paper pasted to the tympan. The spikes of the points should come on this line, and the point-screws must be tightened to prevent the position of the spikes from shifting. There is always a danger of press-points being lowered on the forme and crushing part of the type. Guard against this by watching the descent of the tympan from a view-point level with the forme to see that the points clear the pages, and by always removing the points from the tympan when work for which they are used is finished. In a small press spring points must not be used: they prevent the sheet from lying close to the tympan.

A trial pull is now made to test the register of back and front of the sheet. Two sheets (one to protect the tympan-sheet from "set-off") are laid on the tympan in the area ruled in pencil and pulled with a fairly heavy impression. Then the top one is turned over lengthwise, so that the end that was nearest the forme comes at the outer end of the tympan, and the sheet is laid on again to the pins, or, when points are used, so that the holes made by the points fit over the points again, and an impression is made on the blank side. The sheet is held up to the light to see whether the impressions on the two sides come

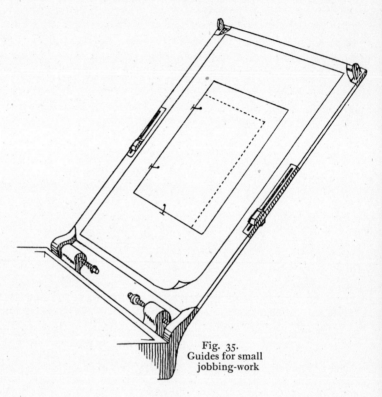

Fig. 35.
Guides for small
jobbing-work

exactly back to back. Generally they do not. If they are not parallel, the trouble may be due to the placing of the pins or the points, or to the chase not being fixed squarely on the bed. The pins or points and the quoins that hold the chase in position should be adjusted until the impressions on either side of the sheet come back to back. If the impression on the tympan-sheet is still wet, dust it with French chalk to prevent it smearing the printed sheets.

Trial pulls are then made to test the strength of the impression. The force of the impact of the platen should be the smallest that is sufficient to make all the letters print clearly.

It must not be so heavy that the reverse side of the sheet is embossed where the letters fall. It is a common failing with amateurs to take too heavy an impression to compensate for bad inking; this is a bad fault, because in reading one side of a sheet the eye is distracted by the bumps caused in printing the other side. The impression should be only just visible from the reverse side of the newly printed sheet. Start the trials with too light an impression and gradually screw the stop back until

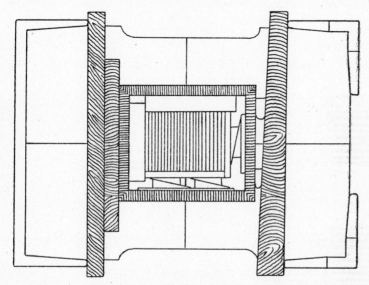

Fig. 36. A method of securing small chases in the bed

the bar can be pulled far enough over to take an impression of the right strength. The stop is then fixed in position with its lock-nut.

The next stage is to cut the frisket. A sheet of strong paper is pasted on the steel frame of the frisket and left to dry. When it has stuck firmly, the overhanging paper is cut away round the edges and the frisket is fastened into its hinge at the outer end of the tympan. An impression from the inked forme is taken on the paper. The frisket is taken out once more and laid on a cutting-surface. All the printed part and a margin of one-eighth of an inch round the four sides of each page of type are cut out with a sharp knife, leaving a network that

F

serves to hold the sheet down on the tympan and to cover the
margins during the impression, and allows only the pages of
type to print.   If there are blank pages or blank half-pages,
they also are protected by leaving the corresponding part of the
paper on the frisket.

When the frisket has been once more fastened in position,
a trial pull is made to test whether the openings are correctly
cut.   Very often it "bites," that is, takes part of the impression
round the edges of the pages, and has to be re-cut here and
there.

When a page is blank or largely blank it often causes the
adjacent edges of neighbouring pages to print too heavily.   To
remedy this, paste pieces of rubber or cork, about five-sixteenths
of an inch thick, on the corresponding parts of the frisket, to
act as supports.   During the impression the supports rest on
the furniture forming the blank page and take the weight of
the platen.   Sometimes the shoulders of the letters in the last
line of a page print, and bearers or frisket-supports can be used
to keep the paper off them.

The press is now ready for printing.   A word must be said
about the preparation of the paper.   Hand-made and mould-
made papers really need damping to take a good impression.
All kinds of uneven-surfaced paper can be made to take a more
complete and even impression when damp.   The damping
should be done, if possible, some time before printing.   With
strong papers it is only necessary to pick up a batch of about
half a dozen sheets and pass them from end to end once fairly
quickly through a basin of water.   When all the paper has
been so treated it is left under a heavy weight, such as a case
of type.   After an hour or so, change the order of the sheets.
It is no good printing until the water has soaked evenly into
the paper.   Certain papers, antiques, cheap fluffy woves, and
arts, disintegrate if wetted and must be printed dry.

The paper must be cut so as to give a sheet small enough to
lie completely on the tympan.   When points are used there is
no need to have any straight edges on the sheets.

It will perhaps be useful to describe the best arrangement
of the accessories to the press during a run of work when two
people work the press.   The ink-slab should stand beside the
staple on the off side of the press, so that the man inking shall

have it on his right. If the work is single-handed, it must be on the other side of the staple. Across the end of the press there should be a long narrow table, to lay paper on. There will be two heaps, one of unprinted paper, just behind the tympan, and another beside it of printed sheets. Behind the tympan there should be a contrivance to support the frisket when it is raised. Unless a permanent fixture is practicable, a substitute can be made of the back of a chair standing on the table. This has the advantage of being movable to a position where it will stop the frisket almost in equilibrium, so that a touch of the finger will make it fall back on the tympan.

The art of inking a forme by hand is not easily or quickly learned. The first step is to form a standard of good inking based on the work of the best printers. Every piece of printing requires special treatment in respect of ink. The different kinds of paper absorb varying quantities of ink. An absorbent paper will take a thin, liquid ink; on some papers such ink never dries. The degree of dampness of the paper when printed affects the problem of how much ink should be used. Even the weather makes a difference.

The forme cannot be evenly inked unless the ink-slab, from which the roller draws its supplies, is covered with an even coating of black. A piece of thick plate-glass about 1ft. by 1ft. 6in. is the best surface on which to spread the ink, but any clean metal or stone surface that is perfectly flat will do. Glass is the easiest to clean. The slab must be firmly fixed on a table. Put a dab of ink at the far end and beat it up thoroughly with a knife. Then put a smear of ink on the roller and roll it out on the slab, spreading it evenly over the whole surface. After every few strokes turn the roller over lengthwise to reverse the direction in which it revolves. Roll the ink from side to side as well as from end to end of the slab. When it is evenly dispersed, ink the forme. Roll from top to bottom of the pages. Begin half-way down a page: not at the top. Run the roller over the type lightly, without using more effort than is needed to keep it running at a constant pressure over the whole of the page; then roll back again. Lift the roller as it comes to the end of the page; do not let it bump off the end. How many times the roller should go over the forme, and how

often fresh ink should be taken from the slab, can only be found
out by experiment. It is bad to ink half a page with one course of
the roller and have to ink the other half later; therefore it is
most necessary to have a roller that is just wide enough to cover
one or two pages comfortably without overlapping the next
page. For use with an Albion with a folio-sized platen, a roller
one foot wide is suitable. The heavier the roller the easier it
is to ink evenly. The smallest sizes of roller do not give good
results except in expert hands. If the forme is rolled lengthwise,
be careful not to let ink get on the tympan.

In inking, the aim is to cover the type evenly. The roller
must not be allowed to dip into the gutters between the pages,
or it will bump on the edges of the type-areas and leave a thick
deposit of ink on them. Type-high bearers made of type-metal
laid outside the chase along two sides of the forme during the
rolling are a great help to getting good, even inking. It is true
that the trouble of putting the bearers in and taking them out
before every impression adds a good deal to the work, but it is
well worth while. Unfortunately, there is sometimes no room
on the bed.

After a time the coating of ink on the slab must be
replenished. It is impossible to lay down rules as to the
frequency with which this should be done, or how much should
be added. So much depends on the amount of type-area in
the forme, the absorbency of the paper and the density of the
ink.

An uneven spread of ink on the slab will cause blotches of
black to appear on the page. The slab must be rolled over
thoroughly after each addition to the supply.

Rollers cannot be too carefully treated. It is impossible to
ink a forme evenly with a roller that has become hard or mis-
shapen with age or ill-treatment. They should be reclothed
with new composition at least once a year. They should be
hung up so that the cylinder is not in contact with anything
when not in use, and never allowed to lie in one position for
hours at a time. They should be wrapped in soft material, not
in paper, when stored. Finally, and this is most important,
they, and the ink slab, should be washed clean after every day's
work.

It is easiest to judge of the effect of inking from a large

letter. It should be black all over, but with no blurring of the outline due to an excess of ink being squeezed over the sides. In judging of the right quantity of ink, concentrate on the largest black space on the sheet.

After inking the forme, lay the paper on the tympan. With the right hand lay the upper end of the sheet against the guide-pins. Then knock the frisket down with a touch of the right hand on the thumb-piece and, holding the thumb-piece of the frisket together with the edge of the tympan, lower the tympan on the forme. Turn the handle of the rounce with the left hand, so as to run the carriage into the press without letting it bump into the stops at the end. Pull the bar over with the right hand. Run out the carriage with the left hand, and raise the tympan with the right.

It must be remembered that any considerable jerking of the carriage is liable to cause a slur. The carriage must run in and out clear of obstructions and smoothly. There are screws on the hinges of the tympan so that it may be moved to left or right; it must be adjusted so as not to knock against the staple as it runs in. Sometimes the fore-end of the tympan jars against the platen. This must be remedied by taking packing from between the tympans, or raising the platen by taking out packing from between it and the lower end of the piston.

A pressman may forget to lay on a sheet and so pull an impression on the sheet pasted on the tympan. In such an event this sheet must be dried with French chalk or taken off and replaced by a clean one, or the backs of a great many succeeding sheets will be spoiled by a set-off of ink.

Slurring of the sheet happens through many different causes. Very often it is due to bumping of the carriage as it runs in. Make sure that the hinges of the tympan are screwed up to prevent side-play. It may be the result of a sagging tympan, for good, clean impressions can only be had with the parchment taut and free from undulations. Unless blank areas in the forme are equipped with bearers, the sagging of the paper will also spoil the impression. Press-points give trouble unless they are flat on the parchment. If they keep the paper from lying on the tympan, they will cause a slur. Other reasons for slurring are to be sought in the forme itself. The type may not be tightly locked up. Unless the type is held firmly upright on its feet, it will be pushed over by the roller, and any leaning is made worse by the pressure of the platen. If the type "hangs" instead of standing upright, the trouble is attributable either to faulty justification or to bad dressing of the forme. Look first to see whether the furniture "binds" instead of pressing against the sides of the pages. Replace any furniture that touches other furniture meeting it at right angles. Often enough, leads too long for the measure give similar trouble. If it is not due to the dressing or the leads, looseness of the type may be explained by bad justification or the falling out of letters. Not infrequently, a punctuation mark at the end of a line gets lost during imposition and its absence passes unnoticed. The pressman should look for these on the reader's proof and make sure they are all there. Lastly, the justification is to be suspected. Short lines must be detected and lengthened. The best way to fill out a line is to loosen the quoins inside the chase and put a piece of strong paper, or visiting card, rather less in width than the body of the type and the height of a space in the line, beside a space between two words. No good craftsman would think of putting packing at the end of a line.

During the run the attention of the pressman will be concentrated on getting equally good inking on all sheets. He should also watch for "rising spaces"—those that stick up and take ink, causing a black mark on the page—and small sorts at the end of a line being pulled out of the forme by the roller.

When one side of all the sheets has been printed, the forme is taken out of the press. It should not be dismantled until both sides are finished, counted, and finally approved, for owing to an accident it may be necessary to reprint. The forme for the second side of the sheet is put in the bed and quoined up in precisely the same position as the first forme. A trial pull is taken on the back of a sheet, preferably one spoiled at the first impression. If register was well made before the start of the run, only small adjustments will be needed to make the two impressions come back to back, assuming that the two formes have been made uniform. The frisket must be examined to make sure that it does not bite the second forme, but if it does, it must be trimmed accordingly. Blank pages in the second forme should be covered with patches on the frisket and supplied with supports.

To correct bad register it may only be necessary to alter the quoins at the corners of the bed. A more serious error can be put right by altering the position of the pins stuck in the tympan. In cases where press-points are being used, it is undesirable to alter their position, but it may be done as a last resource. When the outline of the two impressions has been made to coincide, the margins between the pages must be examined to see that they are equally wide on both formes. If the margins of the second forme are wrong, it must be unlocked and made to conform with the first by means of leads or thin reglets.

In view of possible difficulties in making register with the second side, quite a number of spare sheets should be printed from the first forme for use as trial sheets.

In printing damped paper, the second side must be worked off as soon as the first side is done. The two sides will not look alike if the paper has dried much between-whiles.

When the sheets are completely printed they have to be left to dry. If the paper itself is damp, the sheets should be laid out in small batches in a warm room. In handling freshly printed sheets care must be taken not to slur the impressions by rubbing one sheet sideways against the other.

After drying the sheets, and when the ink is perfectly dry (so that it cannot be smeared with the finger), they should be put between thick boards in a nipping-press or under a heavy weight.

It only remains to explain the way to print in more than one colour. In doing colour-work from type in an Albion press, only one forme is required. If the paper is to be printed damp, the prevailing colour is printed first to get the best impression. The lines that are not in the prevailing colour are underlaid with strips of wood cut from 6-point reglet. Let us assume that there are to be two colours, red and black, and that most of the setting is to be printed in black. The "red" lines are lifted out of the forme as it lies in the press, and strips of reglet are dropped into the empty spaces. Then quads are made up in the composing-stick to the measure of the lines and put in the forme, standing on the wood. A pull is taken on the frisket, and only the black parts of the forme are cut out, so that the frisket guards the sheet wherever red is to appear. When the black printing is finished, the temporary quads are taken out and replaced by the type for the red lines. A new frisket is cut, allowing only the red parts of the forme to print. Since the red part of the forme is higher than the other, some adjustments have to be made to prevent too heavy an impression. Sheets of packing should be taken out of the tympans, and the stop must be adjusted to prevent the bar from coming right over.

Printing illustrations in several colours is more difficult. It is a matter of obtaining very fine register by moving the pins in the tympan, or by shifting the forme.

CHAPTER 10

TYPE AND TYPE-FACES

Type consists of castings from original letters cut in steel. Figure 37 shows the steel punch serving to make the letter h. The tip of the punch being driven into a piece of copper forms

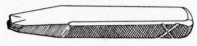

Fig. 37. A punch

a matrix, into which molten type metal is poured to obtain castings reproducing the form of the tip of the punch. The top part of a piece of type represents the steel original: the shank takes its shape from the mould at the end of which the matrix is held during the process of casting.

Type is sold by weight. A consignment of it is called a fount. Founts of any weight from about 5lb. upwards can be bought from typefounders. Every fount is carefully blended of all the necessary "sorts" (as letters, punctuation-marks, figures, asterisks, and all other characters are called), the quantity of each in proportion to the whole depending on the frequency with which it is likely to be used in printing. When a fount is well proportioned the compositor does not run out of any particular sort until the case is fairly low. In making up founts typefounders are guided by a list called a scheme. A typical English scheme for 50lb. of roman type of 12-point body is given opposite. There will, of course, be more letters to an equivalent weight of smaller type, and fewer of type of larger body.

This scheme includes small capitals, spaces and quads, and a few accented letters for quotations in French.

A fount like the one cast to this scheme would be enough to set two small folio pages in English, but if used for French or Latin would not extend to more than half an octavo page, because the compositor would then run out of certain sorts. Both these languages need more of c, i, l, m, p, q, s, u and v than English. Typefounders will always sell small quantities

ENGLISH SCHEME FOR 50 lb. OF 12-POINT ROMAN TYPE
(including spaces and quads)

Lower-case			Capitals			Small Capitals			Figures		
a	-	620	A	-	60	A	-	18	1	-	60
b	-	135	B	-	40	B	-	12	2	-	45
c	-	320	C	-	40	C	-	12	3	-	45
d	-	335	D	-	40	D	-	12	4	-	45
e	-	1000	E	-	70	E	-	24	5	-	45
f	-	250	F	-	40	F	-	12	6	-	45
g	-	160	G	-	40	G	-	12	7	-	45
h	-	470	H	-	40	H	-	12	8	-	45
i	-	620	I	-	40	I	-	17	9	-	45
j	-	60	J	-	25	J	-	6	0	-	60
k	-	60	K	-	25	K	-	6	£	-	10
l	-	300	L	-	40	L	-	12	*Accents*		
m	-	230	M	-	50	M	-	16	â	-	6
n	-	620	N	-	60	N	-	18	ê	-	4
o	-	620	O	-	60	O	-	18	î	-	4
p	-	220	P	-	40	P	-	12	ô	-	4
q	-	50	Q	-	15	Q	-	6	û	-	4
r	-	600	R	-	60	R	-	18	é	-	8
s	-	600	S	-	60	S	-	18	è	-	6
t	-	620	T	-	60	T	-	18	à	-	6
u	-	330	U	-	40	U	-	12	ù	-	4
v	-	110	V	-	30	V	-	9	ç	-	4
w	-	160	W	-	40	W	-	12	*Signs, &c.*		
x	-	40	X	-	12	X	-	6	.	-	280
y	-	160	Y	-	30	Y	-	9	,	-	360
z	-	20	Z	-	10	Z	-	4	;	-	80
&	-	10	Æ	-	4	Æ	-	4	:	-	80
æ	-	5	Œ	-	4	Œ	-	4	-	-	110
œ	-	5							?	-	20
fi	-	35							!	-	20
fl	-	20							(	-	40
ff	-	35							[	-	20
ffi	-	15							—	-	20
ffl	-	15							'	-	100
									*	-	10

Spaces
Thick, 2½ lb. ; Middle, 1¼ lb.
Thin, ¾ lb. ; Hair, ¼ lb. ;
En Quads, 1 lb. ; Em Quad, 1 lb. ;
Large Quads, 5 lb.

of particular letters in packets, but at much higher rates than scale founts.

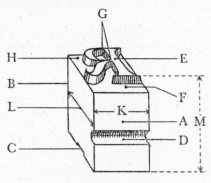

Fig. 38. A piece of type

A. The front   F. The beard
B. The back   G. Counters
C. The feet   H. The shoulder
D. The nick   K. The thickness
E. The face   L. The body
         M. The height-to-paper

Every printer ought to know the names of the various parts of cast letters, and how to describe types of various kinds.

The surface of a piece of type beneath the bottom of a letter is called the front; the opposite surface is the back. The nick is in the front of English type. The measurement from the front to the back of the shank is called the body. All the sorts belonging to a fount are of the same body; but they vary as to the measurement from side to side, called the thickness.

The base on which a piece of type stands is known as its feet. The surface which prints is called the face. The measurement from the feet to the face is the "height-to-paper." All English type is 0.917 of an inch high—the diameter of a shilling. Other countries have heights of their own.

The name of a fount of type is taken from the design of its face and also its body. The body is measured in units called points: the point being 0.01384 of an inch. Thus printers identify types by such names as "10-point Caslon" or "18-point Cheltenham," for example.

The range of types of a single design in many sizes is often referred to as the face. A book is said to be printed in a particular face, Cloister, for example, or Baskerville. We give overleaf a specimen of the Caslon face in various sizes. Each face is cast on several bodies, generally ranging from 6-point to 72-point. Sometimes to obtain the effect of leading without the labour of inserting leads types are cast on a body larger than is necessary.

SPECIMENS

60-point Titling or 72-point Capitals

OF THE TYPES

48-point Titling or 60-point Capitals

CUT BY W. CASLON

36-point Titling or 48-point Capitals

IN ABOUT THE

36-point

years 1720-60

"HE ARRIVED to that perfection so that we may,

24-point

18-point

WITHOUT FEAR OF CONTRADICTION, MAKE THE ASSERTION that a fairer specimen cannot be found in Europe, that is, not in the World." Thus wrote the enthusiastic Mr. Rowe Mores. In 1720 the Society for Promoting Christian Knowledge engaged Caslon to cut an Arabic type. This he DID, AND THE STORY RUNS *that he cut the letters of his own name*

14-point

HIS REPUTATION WAS MADE. His subsequent history is largely the record of the different founts which he cut. Though Caslon began his foundry about 1720, it *WAS NOT UNTIL 1734 THAT HE issued the specimen-sheet, which exhibited*

12-point

RESULTS OF FOURTEEN YEARS OF labour. It shows various founts of type, all cut by Caslon except the Canon roman, which came from Andrews (a "descendant" of the Moxon foundry); the English Syriac, cast from matrices USED FOR THE PARIS *Polyglot Bible of Le Jay, and a pica Samaritan cut by Dummers, a*

10-point

DUTCH MAN. A REPRINT OF THIS SPECIMEN, with a change of imprint, appeared in an edition of Chambers' *Cyclopædia* in 1738, and a note accompanying it says: "The ABOVE WERE ALL CAST IN THE FOUNDRY OF *Mr. W. Caslon, a person who, though not bred in the art of*

8-point

LETTER-FOUNDING, HAS, BY DINT OF GENIUS, ARRIVED at an excellency in it unknown hitherto in England, and which even surpasses anything of the kind done in Holland or elsewhere." Caslon was joined in his business by his son William II, in 1742, and they constantly enlarged their stock of types, both roman and "learned." It was apropos OF THIS EXPANSION THAT A RATHER STARTLING phrase *occurs in Ames' account of their foundry. "The art," he says, "seems to be*

Type-faces are divided into two main classes, one called Old-face and the other Modern-face. The Old-face represents the manner of lettering with the nib held at an angle of 45 degrees with the line, while the Modern-face is based on letters formed with the nib at right angles with the line. The difference between the two styles can be seen in curved strokes. In the Old-face the thickest part occurs above the centre of a right-hand stroke and below the centre of a left-hand one; in the Modern-face the maximum thickness is half-way up the curve. Another difference is in the character of the little cross-lines at the end of the straight strokes, called "serifs." Old-face serifs are blunt and form a wide curve at their junctions with the stems of the letters: "Modern" serifs are long and thin and form right angles with the stems. In Modern-face types the contrast between thick and thin strokes is very marked.

Although the earliest printed books were set in Black Letter, it was not long before the style of type called Roman was evolved. The roman types now in use were copied from the style of writing known as "humanistic," in which the classics were written by the scribes during the late fifteenth and early sixteenth centuries. Nicolas Jenson, a Venetian printer, evolved a roman type about 1470 which is still reckoned as one of the most beautiful and legible that ever existed. Several faces now in commercial use, Cloister, Venezia, and Centaur, for example, are versions of the Jenson design.

These early roman types were not used in conjunction with italics. Italic types were first cut for Aldus, another Venetian, in 1499, but for many years they were used by themselves, and the blending of roman and italic for use together on one page was the idea of the French printers in the early sixteenth century. The italics of Cloister are of a later design than the roman. The French sixteenth-century printers developed a rather narrower and lighter style of letter than the Jenson, and it was equipped with a companion italic. This style is generally called Garamond, after Claude Garamond, a famous type-founder. The design has been reproduced in several contemporary types such as Granjon and Estienne.

In the seventeenth century Holland came to the fore in the world of printing. The Dutch printers varied the French design by making the short letters such as a, c, e, larger in proportion

to such letters as b and p, so that they had less white between
the lines. Caslon and Jenson are survivors of this fashion, the
former being an English type cut by William Caslon in London
about 1720-30, but imitating the best Dutch designs of the
previous century. These are soberer letters than the Garamond,
especially in the italics.

The last Old-face design was that of John Baskerville, a
Birmingham printer, who began his types in 1750. They aimed
much more at elegance than previous designs and their slender-
ness and fineness of line make them hard to print well and liable
to break and wear down. Baskerville's types are unfortunately
now cast in France on bodies different from those used in
England. An imitation by Fry of Bristol cut about 1768 is
still to be had in this country, and we give a specimen of
it on page 25.

From about 1800 to 1870 Old-face types were generally out
of fashion. For high-class work their use was revived about
1840 and they gradually gained favour until now they have
practically banished all others. A type called "Old-style,"
intended to combine the advantages of the Old-face and the
Modern, was introduced in the middle of last century. It is
an easy kind of letter to read and wears well, but it makes a
very pale page. Other essays in the Old-face fashion done
between 1890 and 1910 such as Dolphin and Verona, though
well cut and easy to print and to read, have traces of that queer-
ness which is so often found in the *nouveau-art* of that period.

The best type to use on a damped hand-made paper is an
Old-face such as Caslon's or Fry's. The ink will spread a little
on the wet surface, so that it is better to have letters with thin
strokes, otherwise the impression will be too black. Especially
for use with an Albion press it is better not to have too black
a type because, owing to the padded tympans, the type in
printing sinks into the paper slightly and so leaves a heavy
impression.

For printing cards or smooth-surfaced paper in a dry state,
and particularly in a platen-press, Old-face is too light.
Impressions from a type with thin lines look very bad when
part of the letters fail to come out owing to bad inking and
too weak an impression. To avoid the risk of this, those who
intend to print solely with a small platen-press will be well

advised to buy type such as Cloister without very fine lines. This will be found apt for a wide range of work and beautiful in design.

Some modern "block-letter" types, such as Cable and Granby, are very attractive and are useful for displayed work; but will not serve for printing whole pages.

A B C D E F G H K M

Sans-serif or block-letter capitals

Capital letters are made in innumerable decorated styles, and, sparingly used, help to liven up advertisements and similar work.

A B C   A B C

Ornamental letters

It will be noticed that fi, ff, fl, ffi, ffl, are cast in one piece. This is because the tip of the f juts out beyond the shank and would foul the i and l, and in some founts the f, if put next to them. Anyone who is new to compositor's work will find it difficult to remember to use the f-combinations, and the result will be many broken fs. A piece of type that has a part of the face projecting sideways from the body is said to be "kerned." In handling type especial care should be taken of these "kerned" sorts, such as f, j, ff, *f*, *E*, *W*, for the overhanging parts easily break off.

Sometimes other combinations of letters are cast together, such as ﬆ and ﬅ, *ﬆ*, *ll*, *as*, *us*. These double letters, called "ligatures," are copied from the writing-methods of the scribes, which printers originally set themselves to imitate. In modern practice ligatures are rarely used.

Many types have, in addition to the normal letters, a number of decorative italic letters cut in imitation of flourished penwork. These are called "swash" letters. In "Caslon" there is a particularly full set of them, as follows:

A B C D E G J M N P R T U (for U), in the capitals and *h k v w* among lower-case letters. Of these *E T h* are the original forms for the normal letters; *J T h* were added later.

Of swash letters it may be said that they ought strictly only to be used for beginning words. The spacing between the letters looks irregular when they are used in the middle. This is especially true of v and w, which should on no account be mixed with v and w and used indiscriminately for them. Some types have flourished final letters such as e a s

Besides these there are the combinations QU Qu, cast because the single Q has a long kerned tail that is apt to break.

The parcel of type when it arrives from the typefounder should be put on a sloping galley. The brown paper should be cut through round the sides, and the half that covers the face of the type taken off. The type should rest against the ledges of the galley on two sides. It is much more easily handled and is not so likely to fall off its feet if it is wetted with a sponge or a soft brush before being picked up and laid in the case.

CHAPTER II

PAPERS

Papers are divided into various classes according to the materials from which they are made, the method of their manufacture, and the purpose for which they are intended to be used.

The most durable paper is made from linen and cotton rags. Pure rag paper is becoming increasingly rare, partly owing to the decline in the numbers of cast-off linen collars, from which they used to be largely made. Only luxury papers are made of rag now; those for everyday use consist of esparto grass or wood treated with chemical solvents.

According to the method of making them papers are known as hand-made, mould-made, or machine-made. Hand-made varieties contain rag-pulp and are much more expensive than the others. They are used for drawing, banknotes and the highest grades of writing-, ledger-, and book-papers. A sheet is produced by dipping a square sieve of fine mesh into a vat containing a solution of pounded rag, size, and water; the sieve is then given a peculiar shake, and the sheet is the layer that remains on the sieve after the surplus liquid has percolated through. The edges naturally form a wavy outline on all four sides called the "deckle."

Mould-mades look very like hand-mades, and the best are almost as strong and durable. They are mass-produced on an endless belt of fine-meshed material artificially contrived to produce deckle edges.

Machine-mades are turned out in very long strips, and are cut into sheets with knives. They have rough edges on two sides of the sheet only, which are generally trimmed off before leaving the mill.

Hand-made and mould-made papers contain a good deal of rag; machine-made papers almost invariably consist of esparto grass, or wood-pulp and esparto.

Paper when it is first made has a rough surface. It is very rarely delivered to the printer in this state. Hand-made papers are smoothed by being pressed between hot metal plates.

Machine-mades are put through a machine working on the mangle principle: the more often it passes between rollers the smoother it becomes. Imitation art paper shows how far the process of mangling, or "calendering" as it is technically called, can be carried. The smooth surface necessary for printing is also partly produced by adding some plastic substance, such as china clay, to fill up the interstices of natural paper. Paper intended for writing must have a stiffening of size or other glazing matter to prevent the ink from running as it does in blotting paper. Starch is also used to give thin paper a certain rigidity.

Paper is called either "laid" or "wove." In hand-mades and mould-mades the difference is accounted for by the structure of the sieve on which the layer of pulp is originally formed. The sieve for a laid paper is made of straight wires crossing one another; the others are made on a texture of finer wires inter-woven. If a laid paper be held up to the light, the wire-marks will show plainly. Wove papers hardly show wire-marks. Water-marks are the result of wire-patterns incorporated in the sieve. Some machine-made papers have imitation wire-marks dented into one of the surfaces during the process of drying.

Mould-made paper, like hand-made, can be used for drawing, writing, or printing. Cartridge paper, machine-made with plenty of size, can also be used for all purposes. Other machine-mades are suitable only for printing.

Papers used for printing fall under different heads according to their uses. The chief are book-papers, art papers, imitation art, and cover papers. Besides these, the various kinds of paper used for stationery, including such things as letter-paper, account books, and partly printed forms, are kept in all printers' warehouses.

Book-papers are hand-made, mould-made, or machine-made. The best hand-mades such as Whatman or Unbleached Arnold, for example, are used as much for drawing as for printing, but printers call them book-papers. The strongest machine-mades also come under this head. A class that is much used is that with the Antique finish. These are very lightly pressed, so that they have a rough, loose texture. They have the disadvantage of being dissimilar on the two sides, the under side being rather difficult to print on. There are good book-papers called "Parchments" that are fairly smooth on both sides and of medium hardness with good wearing qualities.

"Printing" papers are always machine-made from wood-pulp or esparto grass, or a combination of the two. They are not as strong as rag papers in texture, and are made in various thicknesses. Their use is chiefly for circulars and jobs for which a durable material is not needed. Art paper is made from wood-pulp coated on both sides with china clay and then calendered, thereby giving it a polished, glossy surface. It is the only medium for printing the finest half-tone blocks. Imitation art, made of esparto and wood-pulp heavily rolled to give it a polished surface, can be used for all but the finest half-tone blocks. The same remark applies to super-calendered, excepting that it is all wood-pulp. These are generally used for illustrated magazines. Imitation art, super-calendered, and "printings" are the cheapest sorts of paper.

Cover papers may be made of any material and by any process. They are thick, strong, and usually coloured. Often enough they are finished in curious styles imitating the textures of cloth, leather, wood or other alien substances.

Special papers made for stationery include azures, cream laids and cream woves, banks and bonds, and loans. Forms and books for accounts are generally printed on the blue-dyed paper called azure. Loan is a very strong, smooth paper resembling vellum, used chiefly for legal documents. Letter papers of the highest class are hand-made or mould-made. Among machine-made writing papers cream laids are much used for note-books and cheap letter-paper. Cream woves, "parchments" and "vellums," like thin cartridge paper in appearance, form the common class of private letter-papers. Business correspondence is more often done on bank or bond paper (the two names are used somewhat indiscriminately), a thin, hard, springy, transparent variety that is so strongly sized that it is most difficult to print on.

There are certain technical particulars in which printing and stationery papers differ. For one thing, the sheets are made in different sizes.

Common sizes of book and printing-papers are:

Double Crown ...	...	...	...	...	20 ×30	inches
Double Demy ...	...	...	...	...	22½×35	,,
Double Royal ...	...	...	...	...	25 ×40	,,
Quad. Crown ...	...	...'	...	...	30 ×40	,,

(but sheets half these sizes are obtainable).

Stationery papers are generally of the following sizes:

Medium	...	...	...	...	18 ×23	inches
Large Post	...	...	...	...	16½×21	,,
Post	...	...	...	...	16 ×20	,,
Foolscap	...	...	...	...	13½×17	,,

A ream of book-paper is 516 sheets; a ream of writing paper 480, or 20 quires. In this respect all hand-made papers are like stationery, a ream of them being 480 sheets. Paper is always purchased by the ream or the quire.

An important side-line is the class that printers call "boards," and that most people speak of as cardboard. Boards are either pulpboard or pasteboard. Pulpboard is a homogeneous whole made of fine wood-pulp and esparto: paste boards are several sheets of paper stuck together. The latter are classified by the number of sheets that go to make them, thus: two-sheet, six-sheet pasteboard, and so forth. For printing, white pulpboard is almost always used, pasteboard being used only when a stiffer and more durable material is required.

These are the most important varieties that concern the letterpress printer.

The needs of school-printers will probably be satisfied by a very few kinds of paper. The quantities dealt with will not be so large as to make it advisable to buy inferior varieties for the sake of cheapness. Unless very fine half-tone blocks are to be printed it will not be necessary to stock art paper (which deteriorates unless kept dry and at an even temperature). Up to 120-screen these blocks give satisfactory results on a smooth book-paper. The authors suggest a machine-made paper of the sort called "Parchment" as a useful all-round stock that is easy to print, presentable and inexpensive.

A mould-made paper is equally useful and more beautiful, but dearer. One of these of medium thickness is excellent for work

SIZES OF PRINTING PAPERS

Name	Full Sheet	Folio	4to.	8vo.
CROWN	15×20	15×10	$10 \times 7\frac{1}{2}$	$7\frac{1}{2} \times 5$
DOUBLE CROWN	20×30	20×15	15×10	$10 \times 7\frac{1}{2}$
DEMY	$17\frac{1}{2} \times 22\frac{1}{2}$	$17\frac{1}{2} \times 11\frac{1}{4}$	$11\frac{1}{4} \times 8\frac{3}{4}$	$8\frac{3}{4} \times 5\frac{5}{8}$
DOUBLE DEMY	$22\frac{1}{2} \times 35$	$22\frac{1}{2} \times 17\frac{1}{2}$	$17\frac{1}{2} \times 11\frac{1}{4}$	$11\frac{1}{4} \times 8\frac{3}{4}$
MEDIUM	18×23	$18 \times 11\frac{1}{2}$	$11\frac{1}{2} \times 9$	$9 \times 5\frac{3}{4}$
DOUBLE MEDIUM	23×36	23×18	$18 \times 11\frac{1}{2}$	$11\frac{1}{2} \times 9$
ROYAL	20×25	$20 \times 12\frac{1}{2}$	$12\frac{1}{2} \times 10$	$10 \times 6\frac{1}{4}$
DOUBLE ROYAL	25×40	25×20	$20 \times 12\frac{1}{2}$	$12\frac{1}{2} \times 10$
FOOLSCAP	$13\frac{1}{2} \times 17$	$13\frac{1}{2} \times 8\frac{1}{2}$	$8\frac{1}{2} \times 6\frac{3}{4}$	$6\frac{3}{4} \times 4\frac{1}{4}$
LARGE POST	$16\frac{1}{2} \times 21$	$16\frac{1}{2} \times 10\frac{1}{2}$	$10\frac{1}{2} \times 8\frac{1}{4}$	$8\frac{1}{4} \times 5\frac{1}{4}$
IMPERIAL	22×30	22×15	15×11	$11 \times 7\frac{1}{2}$

NOTE. Books and pamphlets when trimmed will be about $\frac{1}{4}$ in. shorter and $\frac{1}{8}$ in. narrower than the sizes given above.

of a literary character. For big undertakings, seeing that much time and care will be spent on them, many will think hand-made paper worth extra expense. These and mould-mades are almost certain to need damping.

A selection of coloured cover papers will be a great resource for adding a decorative note.

CHAPTER 12

LAY-OUT AND DESIGN

There is a pleasing orderliness that distinguishes any piece of manual work faithfully rendering a preconceived plan. Printing includes several intricate processes, and calls for rather specially detailed forethought and planning. A carefully drawn up scheme serves as a double check: firstly it tests the feasibility of the ideas embodied in it, and secondly it ensures that the design will be kept in view by those engaged in the various departments of the work.

The first steps in planning printed work take place in the imagination, and it is only when well-defined notions have been formulated that a scheme can prudently be committed to paper. The preliminary and experimental work generally takes two forms, a specimen showing size, shape and kind of paper or other material, called the "dummy," and a lay-out showing how the printed matter is to be fitted into the space available.

The choice of material and of its size and shape gives scope for inventiveness and demands a wide experience of the market as well as the techniques of printing and binding. The resources of school printers will be rather limited as to the number of kinds of paper and boards that they can keep in stock, but the size can be varied.

Certain limitations on the choice of paper are to be noted. Half-tone blocks, for example, need a highly calendered paper, and even line- and wood-blocks achieve their best effects on smooth paper. To a certain extent this is also true of type. Rough paper, however, is agreeable in itself and if damped will take a good sharp impression from hand-cut types. There are occasions, such as concerts and dramatic entertainments, when crackling paper is a nuisance, so literature prepared for them should be printed on limp paper. Sometimes considerations of postal rates makes lightness essential: in others where the work is to be constantly handled, some heavy rigid material is desirable.

Besides such practical considerations there are also purely

aesthetic grounds for preferring one kind of paper on account of its colour, substance, or texture. It is curious to note that a scientific investigator came to the conclusion that pale green paper was less fatiguing to the eyes than any other background for black print.

The size of the page and the way of folding the sheet should be thought out with a view to economising paper. Occasionally square or oblong pages are more suitable than the ordinary tall and narrow ones. The expense of fastening several leaves together with thread or wire staples may be saved by using a folder.

The dummy will give a general idea of the appearance of the finished work. The lay-out is a sketch of the type-setting to serve as a guide to the compositor. Experience tends to show that even the most straightforward settings had better not be begun without a lay-out.

The lay-out is generally drawn actual size with the words and decorative features sketched in pencil. Written directions for the kind of type and amount of spacing between the lines are added in the margin. Considerable latitude should be left to the compositor, who will often be able to improve on the rough sketch.

Reduced to its simplest terms the art of laying out may be said to be the arrangement of printed matter so as to be read most easily. On a well laid-out page, column advertisement, or other space allocated to printing the reader finds what he wants to read without effort. If there is one word in the space, it is put in the position where he first looks for it, and it is of such a size that he can take it in at a glance but without straining his eyesight. A full page may either be continuous matter, such as a page of a book, or "display," such as an advertisement. In an ordinary page the lines should not be so long that the reader loses his way and reads the same line twice over, nor so short that the words have to be either too close together or too far apart and too often broken between two lines. In displayed matter two or three prominent words should give a fair idea of the purport of the work.

In planning continuous reading-matter the first step is to settle the measure. The proportion of type-area to the page can best be judged by eye, taking into account the character of the type and the amount of leading. When the block of reading-matter is very black, owing to the type being a heavy face and without leads, the margins should be of maximum width: a page set in lighter type or one widely leaded can occupy more of the page without making the margins look cramped. It will be found that in most cases the margins on either side will together amount to approximately a third of the width of the page.

The ideal line from a reader's point of view is one that contains an average of from eight to ten words. From a printer's point of view this is rather too short: it gives rise to a great many broken words at the ends of the lines and leads to much variation in the spacing between the words. A line that is rather too long for comfortable reading is much improved by leading.

There are rules for determining the proportion of margin on each of the four sides of a page, but they are not to be trusted. The most that can be said is that the margin at the back is the narrowest, that at the head comes next in ascending order of size, then the one at the fore-edge, and the margin at the foot is widest. The reasonable basis on which margins are planned is as follows: Two facing pages ought to form the unity that printers call the "opening." If the type were centred on each page, instead of being nearer to the back, the opening would consist of two disjointed halves. The head margin is narrower than at the foot partly because the optical centre of a page is always above the geometrical centre, and partly because the reader's thumb goes in the foot margin and will obscure the reading-matter unless the margin is of a generous size.

When the margins of a book have been settled, the chief points of interest are the arrangements of the title-page and the treatment of the beginnings of chapters or other sections. The title-page falls under the head of "display" and will be dealt with later.

The headings of chapters and the opening words are a field for typographical ingenuity. Even if the type available is restricted to one fount, considerable variety of treatment is still possible. The old fashion of beginning a new chapter one third of the way down the page is becoming rare. Many modern experts favour beginning at the head of a page. The usual custom is to set the first word in capitals, not indented, but a three- or four-line drop initial, a large initial standing in line with the following word, the opening word in small capitals, or the whole line in capitals are all quite satisfactory. For large initials titling type is much preferable; the ordinary capital leaves an ugly space beneath it and refuses to range, as an initial should, with lines of matter at top and bottom. Failing special type for initials fine effects can be got with letters cut on wood or linoleum. A daring essay in these will make or mar a piece of printing. The title of the heading should, logically, be more conspicuous than such lines as "Chapter"; usually the heading in capitals, and the word "Chapter" in small capitals, of the fount used for the text are perfectly suitable.

AN ESSAY ON MORALS

Section 1 : Our Roman Morality

EUROPEAN civilisation has always been dominated by the influence of the Roman Empire. The Romans were deficient on the artistic and on the religious side. They adopted the Greek culture, and afterwards the Christian religion, when they found that mere organisation and administrative efficiency could not serve to maintain the unity of the Empire. But they accepted them as tributaries and servants of imperialism, while despising profoundly both Greeks and Christians. Greek art

Fig. 39. A section-opening with a home-made initial.

Until about 1800 it was usual to put a strip of ornament, called a "headband," across the top of a page beginning a new chapter. In the case of a less important break a line of flowers used often to separate two sections. The degree of emphasis on the beginning of a new chapter or other division of a book should be related to the extent to which the sense is broken. Headings of equal status should be treated uniformly throughout.

Title-pages are an example of the kind of work that printers call "display." It also includes advertisements, posters, invitations, and similar things laid out with an eye to decorative effect, as opposed to "continuous matter," in which all words are treated alike, and no breaks are artificially made by spacing. The decorative effect is not the only thing to be considered in laying out displayed settings. The varying importance of words and phrases has also to be stressed by the use of different kinds of letters and by spacing. The reader is helped by making the most important words claim particular attention and by breaking the matter up into separate lines of phrases that need to be taken together. The special feature of a displayed page is that it forms a unity. Each line plays its part as a member of a larger whole: it must not be in any way out of harmony with the rest. The difficulty is to envisage the whole setting before deciding how to treat the parts, and yet to arrive at a scheme that gives each part a fair share of effectiveness. The commonest arrangement is to divide the matter into lines that form natural groups of words and then to set the lines in type of several sizes so that the biggest comes near the top and another bold line near the bottom. In this arrangement the outline of the work makes a shape like an hour-glass with the bigger globe at the top. Two variants of the scheme are shown on pages 104 and 105.

A kind of display that is in favour just now is the squared-up setting. In this the matter is made to fill a rectangle, often enclosed in a border of rules or ornament. To help to make the lines of equal length words set in capitals are often interspaced with hair or thin spaces between the letters. This letter-spacing is an expedient that is very useful in display to make a line easily readable and equal in colour to the text; but it should only be done to words in capitals.

It is difficult to afford useful guidance to beginners in setting miscellaneous jobs. Each piece of work has an appropriate manner, and no rules will hold good universally. Experiment is really the only method of approach to jobbing work. The following are a few practical hints:

A TREATISE
ON
TURNIPS

DESIGNED TO PROVE THAT THEY ARE
the most excellent of vegetables

AND

Giving directions for their cultivation
and preparation for the table

BY

GEORGE HIGGINS

LONDON
THE EXCELSIOR PRESS
1931

A TREATISE ON TURNIPS

designed to prove that they are the most
excellent of vegetables, and giving
directions for their cultivation
and preparation for the table

BY

GEORGE HIGGINS

LONDON · 1931
THE EXCELSIOR PRESS

Mixture of type-faces is regarded as a howler by purists; and, indeed, if it is done, it must be done tastefully. An out-line letter, a script or a black-letter may be used with any ordinary fount, but two book-founts seldom mix well. The work of any professional printer in a small way of business will probably afford an example of the inartistic atmosphere produced by indiscriminate mixture of types.

Generally, lines of displayed matter, whether big or small, should be spaced equally far apart.

Underlining words with rules to emphasise them is a practice frowned on by good printers. The important word had much better be made conspicuous in some other way, as by being set in capitals spaced apart or by being put in a prominent position.

In displayed work punctuation should be little used; a comma or other stop at the end of an isolated line is not neces-sary and spoils the balance of it. A full stop at the end of a title is also out of place. The style of setting can be relied on to show that the matter does not read on after the last word.

Pieces of rule or ornament put between the lines on a dis-played page have an old-fashioned air. It is more in accordance with present-day practice to do without them, and rely on spacing only to show breaks in the matter.

Two great rules in display are (a) to emphasise words in order of importance, and (b) not to separate phrases that should be read as continuous. Both the decorative and the emphasising functions of display are easily overdone: a restrained manner has the advantage of gaining approval over a longer period. Printers have to beware of allowing advertisers' lay-out men to force the pace for them when they are setting things that people *want* to read.

The fact of possessing a limited range of types does not prove to be as hampering as might be supposed. It certainly acts as a stimulus to ingenuity in using capitals, small capitals, lower-case, roman and italic, each to the best advantage. Unless large notices are wanted it will be found possible to set work of all kinds with a fount of 12-point roman and italic. Larger sizes and initial letters are of course a help to striking effects, but they are by no means necessary. A specimen setting of the opening page of a magazine in 12-point Caslon is given here. Woodcut letters and devices will greatly enlarge the scope of a printer working with a single fount.

In laying out small pieces of displayed matter for letter-headings, invitations, announcements and the like it is best not to start with a preconceived notion of what the setting should look like, but to work it out step by step so as best to satisfy the special need which the printed word is to supply. For instance in a programme for a play or other function the type should be heavily leaded in order to be legible in a bad light. A letter-heading should not encroach on the space needed for writing nor be in large type that will look out of scale with the handwriting. Private stationery, such as invitations and the like, should not be so boldly displayed as commercial work: it should aim at looking discreet and distinguished. Notices of meetings or of objects lost and found should be as striking and obvious as possible. Such considerations as these should come first. Nevertheless precedents taken from the work of good printers are a great inspiration, and there is no reason to think that imitation in early stages will prevent a man from doing original work later on when he has learnt how to get the effects that he wants with the material at his disposal. Books like the following containing reproductions of printed work will be found increasingly interesting with growing knowledge of the subject:

The Fleuron, edited by S. Morrison and O. Simon. 6 vols. London, 1925-1930.

Printing of To-day, by Simon and Rodenberg. London: Peter Davies, 1928.

Histoire de l'Imprimerie par l'Image, by Marius Audin. Paris: Jonquières, 1928.

So also will the permanent exhibitions at the British Museum and the Victoria and Albert Museum.

It is submitted for the consideration of designers and lay-out men that their true function is not to obtain uncommon and original effects by using type, ink and paper in new ways so much as to make sure that the natural and inherent beauty of their material shall be fully apparent. Far-fetched or

"NEWS   January,

FROM   1931

WICKHAM"   Vol. 1, No. 3

Printed and published at Holywell School

Contents:

THE SCHOOL RAT WEEK

RETURNING one night lately from an evening with his friends in the village, "George" thought he saw a number of rats coming from under the bicycle-shed. He reported this to the Matron and it was decided that a rat week should be put in hand. On Monday, November 1st, proceedings were begun by a lecture on "Rodents" by Mr. Arbuthnot, who described to us the life-history of the average rat, giving particulars of its diet, habits of breeding and favourite haunts. It was therefore equipped with full knowledge of the enemy that we opened the campaign that afternoon. A party, led by Griggs, who is an expert

Fig. 40. A one-fount setting

laboured lay-outs soon become irritating, especially to their authors. The work of the greatest masters of printing shows that printed matter should fall into its natural shape, should be unpretentious and economical, if it is to make a lasting appeal.

CHAPTER 13

ILLUSTRATION

It is suggested that pictures, if they are used at all, should be more in the nature of decorations than illustrations in the strict sense of a means of helping the reader to visualise the story. That is to say they should be considered as part of the printing, like the choice of the type and the lay-out of the page. Early printed books provide delightful examples of pictures, often comically primitive as representations of their subject, that harmonise with the letterpress and make the book as a whole look interesting and rich. One or two artists have made illustrations that do not disturb the effect of the printed page, and yet are so convincing in realism of a simple kind that even a child could not find fault with them. Holbein's woodcuts for the Old Testament are a case in point.

Technical methods of rendering illustrations are divisible into two main classes: blocks and other methods. Blocks present the printing-surface in relief; the others have the part to be printed either sunk below the white parts or level with them.

To printers blocks have the advantage of convenience. Small cuts that are inset in the type-measure are put in the composing-stick and the lines of type are set by their side. Also they stand the same height as type and can be inked at the same time as the letters. This means that the addition of an illustration does not involve any extra work to the printer, except the additional care that is needed to bring out details and subtle effects.

There are three kinds of blocks: wood-blocks, line-blocks and half-tone blocks.

The great usefulness and wide scope of wood-blocks as a means of printing pictures may be judged from the fact that until about 1890, apart from intaglio engravings or etchings involving special methods of impression, they were the only means of illustration known. Nowadays woodcuts suggest to most people the blocks cut by artists to their own designs and used chiefly for illustrating expensive books and Christmas cards, but it is surprising to find how much work is still done

ILLUSTRATION   111

by professional wood-engravers for commercial purposes, for instance, illustrations in catalogues and small devices such as trade-marks.

Other methods of reproducing pictures, lithography, copper-engravings or etchings, collotype and stencilling, involve a separate method of printing and special apparatus.

Woodcuts or lino-cuts are the most satisfactory means of illustration to non-professional printers, because they can be

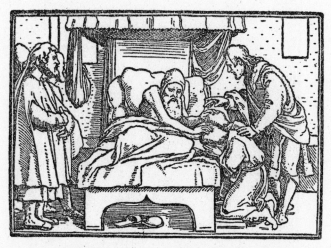

Fig. 41. Illustration to the Old Testament, by Holbein the Younger.
An example of the black-line technique

made by amateurs without mechanical appliances. The art of linoleum cutting is similar, but incapable of rendering fine lines: a lino-cut is practically a woodcut on a larger scale.

There are two main classes of wood-blocks; firstly the black-line block, or woodcut proper, secondly the white-line block or wood-engraving. Both kinds are suitable for book-illustration. The black-line method—the one in which the picture is rendered in thin black lines left in relief on the wood, has the advantage of harmonising better with type, because there are few large masses of black, and the medium, black line, is the same as that used for the letters. The old books illustrated with black-line woodcuts produced by knife-cuts on the plank, not the end of the grain, look more unified in treatment than modern books with white line engravings.

The possibility of using colour wood-blocks should also be borne in mind. Linoleum blocks for two or three-colour effects are an excellent means of decorating the paper covers of booklets, magazines and programmes.

Fig. 42. An illustration by A. Krávchenko, done in the white-line manner

In printing wood-blocks there are a few special points to remember. They need more ink than type. When there is a block in a page also containing type it is inevitable that the type should be rather over-inked if the block is to appear rightly inked.

Blocks of all kinds generally need underlaying to bring them to the proper height. The wooden blocks sold as raw material are rather less than type-high, but when they are printed in the

ILLUSTRATION 113

same forme as type they should be higher than the letters, by about the thickness of tissue paper. Impressions should be taken from the forme and the block should have paper pasted on its under side until the impression appears to bear equally on the block and the letterpress: then the block should have an extra sheet of tissue paper put under it. During the run the block may sink beneath the level of the type and need more under-laying. If the block is lower on one side than another extra pieces of paper should be pasted under the low part to bring it level.

Wood-blocks must never be washed with water or they will warp and, if made of several pieces joined together, will be likely to crack. They should be cleaned with paraffin after use. If they are put away, it is a wise precaution to soak them well with paraffin first, to fit them to resist damp.

Process line-blocks are made by coating zinc or copper with a sensitive film, photographing on to it and etching away the whites while preserving the blacks. It is possible to use the same process substituting drawing with ink on the zinc for photography. From an artistic point of view etched line-blocks are rather second-rate: the lines never have a really clean outline. They are useful for diagrams in technical books and for maps. Hand drawn and etched zinc blocks can be made by amateurs without expensive appliances, but the results are not very good. School-printers are advised when they need line-blocks to have them made by professional engravers. They cost 8d. per square inch, with a minimum of 14 square inches (10s. 2d.).

The illustrations to this book, except that on p. 114, are reproduced by means of line-blocks.

Half-tone blocks are used chiefly as a means of printing from photographic originals. It is not possible for amateurs to make them. The printing-surface consists of black dots varying in size and occasional patches of solid black for absolutely dark tones. The dots are produced by a glass screen ruled with intersecting lines very close together, through which the image is projected on to the negative. The block itself is made from a sheet of copper coated with a thin sensitised film. An exposure from the negative is made on this film, and the plate is subjected to an acid treatment which leaves the black

A 120-screen half-tone

dots in relief. The distance between the centres of the dots depends on the fineness of the screen used. The finest screens have 225 parallel lines to the inch. A block made with this screen is called a 225-screen block. The screens generally used are 55, 60, 75, 85, 100, 120, 133, 150, 175. The finer the screen the more closely does the impression from the block resemble the original. 175- and 150-screen blocks can only be printed on art paper. 133- and 120-screen blocks are used for imitation art paper, 120- and 100-screens may be used for machine-made papers with a hard, smooth finish. The coarser screens are for newspaper work. Half-tone and line blocks may be reduced or enlarged in relation to the original. The outline can be rectangular, oval or round; "cut-out," i.e., with the object silhouetted on a white ground; or "vignetted," that is with the background suppressed and shading put in instead, gradually dying away around the object. Squared-up half-tones, that is those that reproduce the whole of an original within a given rectangle, cost 1s. 2d. per square inch, with a minimum of 14 square inches (18s. 6d.). In ordering half-tone blocks the following particulars should be given: size of finished impression required, calibre of screen, what part of the original is to be reproduced, whether the block is to be squared-up, oval, cut-out, or vignetted, and

ILLUSTRATION   115

whether or not it is to be surrounded with a border of rules.

Coloured illustrations may be printed from line-blocks or half-tone blocks. These must have a separate block for each colour. Very delightful simple effects from colour line-blocks are to be seen in illustrations by the late Claud Lovat Fraser.

The stencil method of colouring illustrations is well adapted for school purposes. This method is very little used by professional printers by reason of its slowness; nevertheless, it has great possibilities. The basis is a black and white drawing rendered by means of a line-block or wood-cut. The colours are added in water-colour dabbed on with a brush through stencils. It is a technique better suited to abstract designs than pictorial illustration.

APPENDIX I

A GLOSSARY OF PRINTING

ALBION PRESS   ..   An iron hand printing-press introduced about 1815, being really an improved version of the old wooden press. The type lies on a horizontal surface, and pressure is applied by another horizontal surface.

ASCENDERS ..   ..   The strokes of certain lower-case letters, such as b, d, projecting above the level of such letters as x or n. Sometimes used as a name for letters that have these strokes.

ASTERISK   ..   ..   A star-shaped sort cast so as to align with the tops of the capitals, used chiefly as a reference mark.

AUTHOR'S CORRECTIONS   Rectifying mistakes caused by the author's fault, or embodying his additions to the matter contained in the proof. This is done at the author's expense.

BACK MARGINS   ..   The margins adjoining the binding of the book.

BEARD   ..   ..   The space below a character whose face does not extend to the bottom of the body. See fig. 38, p. 87.

BEARERS   ..   ..   Strips of type-metal of the same height as type and about 5/8 in. wide put in the forme to make the ink-rollers run smoothly. Also pieces of cork stuck to the frisket on an Albion press to prevent the paper from sagging into blank spaces in the forme.

BED .. .. .. The surface against which the feet of the type rest in the press.

BIND .. .. .. Furniture is said to bind if it presses against other furniture in a forme when it is locked up, and so prevents the type from being squeezed tight.

BLACK LETTER .. An old fashion of letters formerly used for books throughout Northern Europe, of which German *Fraktur* is a variety, now displaced by roman except for occasional ecclesiastical purposes, *e.g.* 𝔄 𝔅 ℭ

BODKIN .. .. A pointed instrument used for picking type out of the forme.

BODY .. .. .. The measurement of a piece of type from back to front. All the type belonging to a single fount has the same body. See fig. 38, p. 87.

BOLD .. .. .. A type with thick strokes, used in commercial display work in conjunction with ordinary type to draw attention to particular words or to emphasise headings.

BOX .. .. .. A compartment in the case.

BRACE .. .. A sign of varying length used to show connection between several items, *e.g.* ⌒⌒

BRASS RULE .. Type-high strips of brass of various thicknesses used for printing straight lines. Brass rules are cut to standard lengths.

BRAYER .. .. Another name for a small hand ink-roller.

BREAK A WORD .. To set one or more syllables of a word at the end of a line followed by a hyphen and the remainder at the beginning of the line beneath.

BROADSIDE .. .. A sheet of any size which is printed on one side only.

CARET .. .. .. The sign used by proof-readers to indicate an omission.

CASE .. .. .. A shallow wooden tray divided into compartments in which printers keep type. See fig. 6, p. 27.

CHASE .. .. .. A rectangular frame of steel or iron in which type is locked prior to its being put on the printing machine. See fig. 33, p. 72.

CLOTHE A ROLLER To coat the spindle with a cylinder of roller-composition.

CLUMPS .. .. Leads having a thickness equivalent to 6 or 12 points. They serve the same purpose as leads.

COLUMBIAN PRESS An iron hand printing-press invented in America about 1810. Similar to the Albion, but with weights instead of a spring for raising the platen.

COMPOSING STICK A tool used by compositors in arranging type in lines. It consists of a flat metal surface surrounded on three sides by strips of metal, two being at right angles to the other, one being movable so that the same stick may be used for lines of various lengths. See fig. 7, p. 29.

COPY .. .. .. The manuscript or similar original matter given to the printer to set in type.

CORRECTING IN THE METAL Rectifying the mistakes marked by the proof-reader by picking out wrong letters from the type that has been set and putting the right ones in their place.

COUNTER   ..   ..   The hollow in type enclosed by parts of the face in relief, as in the middle of O.

CROTCHET   ..   ..   A square bracket.

CROWN   ..   ..   One of the regular sizes (15 × 20 inches) in which full sheets of paper are made. (Double Crown 20 × 30 inches.)

DECKLE-EDGE   ..   The uneven edges of hand-made and mould-made papers.

DESCENDERS   ..   The strokes of some lower-case letters, such as p and q, coming below the level of such letters as x and n. Sometimes used as a name for the letters that have these strokes.

DEMY   ..   ..   ..   One of the regular sizes of paper. A full sheet measures 17½ × 22½ inches. (Double Demy 22½ × 35 inches.)

DIDOT BODY   ..   A body based on the Didot point (0.0148 of an inch). Most of the type used on the Continent is cast on Didot bodies.

DISPLAY   ..   ..   To set matter with an eye to decorative effect or to attracting attention.

DISTRIBUTION   ..   Dispersing type back again into the case after printing has been done.

DOUBLE   ..   ..   The common mistake in composing type of setting a word or phrase twice over.

DRIVE OUT   ..   ..   To occupy much space sideways. A wide type is said to drive out. Also a direction to compositors to put wide spaces between words.

ELECTRO. (ELECTROTYPE)   A reproduction of a line or lines of type, or of a block, made in copper deposited by electrolysis.

EM	Width equivalent to the body of a fount of type—12pt. unless otherwise stated.
EN	Width equivalent to half the body of a fount of type—of 12pt. unless otherwise stated.
END-STICK	The piece of furniture adjoining the quoins along the shorter side of a forme. See *Side-stick.*
EVEN SMALL CAPITALS	A direction to set words entirely in small capitals, without initial capitals.
FACE	The flat surface of a piece of type that prints. Also used to mean the design of a type, *e.g.* Caslon is a beautiful face.
FLOWER	An ornament cast as type.
FLY-SHEET	A sheet of paper folded down the middle, making four pages.
FOLIO	The printed figure or figures used to distinguish each page and to show its place in the sequence of pages.
FOOLSCAP	A size in which writing-paper is made. A full sheet measures 13½ × 17 inches.
FORE-EDGE MARGIN	The margin down the outer side of a page.
FORME	A unit consisting of one or more pages of type intended to be put in the press and printed on one side of a single sheet of paper. A "naked" forme consists only of pages of type tied up with string. A "dressed" forme consists of pages of type with furniture between and around them. A locked-up forme is a rigid collection of type and furniture wedged into a chase.

FOUNT .. .. .. A consignment of type of one body and design made up of all the letters and other necessary characters in the proportions in which each is likely to be needed.

FRAME .. .. .. A rack containing type cases and with a sloping top at which composing is carried out.

FRISKET .. .. A thin metal frame covered with paper hinged on the tympan of an Albion press, serving to protect the margins from becoming smeared with ink during the impression and to pull the paper away from the type when the tympan is raised. Also the metal strips (sometimes called the "grippers") hinged at the base of the platen of a platen press to hold the paper down and pull it away from the type after the impression.

FURNITURE .. .. There are two kinds of furniture, metal and wooden. Both have the same function, which is to fill up the blank spaces in a forme around and between the pages of type. Furniture surrounding type formes is known as dressing.

GALLEY .. .. A tray with an open end on which type is placed after it has been composed in lines in the composing stick. Pages are "made up" on galleys.

GALLEY-PROOF .. A proof taken from type before it has been made up in pages.

GUILLOTINE .. A machine with a sharp knife for cutting paper and cards.

GUTTER .. .. A space between two pages in a forme occupied by furniture.

HAIR LINES .. .. The fine lines in type reproducing "up-strokes" in writing.

HALF-TITLE .. .. A displayed type-setting, showing simply the name of a book or part of a book, occupying a whole page, generally preceding the full title-page.

HALF-TONE BLOCK A metal plate on which a negative has been photo-mechanically engraved. The subject is photographed through a closely ruled screen which breaks up the tone values and reproduces the varying qualities of light and shade of the original.

HANGING FIGURES Figures in which the 3, 4, 5, 7 and 9 project below the 1, 2 and 0, and the 6 and 8 project above.

HANGING TYPE .. Type is said to "hang" when it does not stand level on its feet in the forme.

HEAD .. .. .. The top of a book or a page.

HOUSE
CORRECTIONS Rectifying mistakes made by the printer. This is done at the printer's expense.

IMPOSING-SURFACE Also known as "the stone." A flat, firm surface to which type is transferred from the galley, and where it is locked up in the chase.

IMPRINT .. .. The printer's name and address printed on the work done in his office.

INDENT .. .. To begin a line with a space, generally at the beginning of a paragraph. The space appearing on the paper is called an indention.

INFERIOR .. .. A sort cast on the bottom of the body so that it comes below the level of short letters such as a or n.

KEEP IN .. .. To occupy little space sideways. A narrow type is said to keep in. Also a direction to a compositor to put narrow spaces between words.

KERN .. .. .. A projecting part of the face of type over-hanging the shank.

KEY .. .. .. A tool used for tightening metal quoins.

LARGE POST .. .. One of the sizes in which paper is made. A full sheet measures 16½ × 21 inches.

LEADERS .. .. Type used for printing a series of dots to guide the eye from one point on the page to another.

LEADS .. .. .. Strips of type-metal of varying thickness, less than type-high, used for interlinear spacing of lines of type. (Pronounced to rhyme with "reds.")

LETTER-SPACE .. To put hair or thin spaces between the letters of a word.

LIGATURES .. .. Two letters with a connecting stroke cast on one shank, such as ct st reproducing forms used by the scribes who wrote books in the Roman hand. Often, but not strictly correctly, used for combinations such as fi, ffl, Qu, that exist for the printer's convenience.

LOCKING-UP .. .. Fitting quoins in a forme and tightening them so as to hold the type and furniture of a forme firmly in position inside a chase.

LOWER-CASE LETTERS — The ordinary letters a, b, c, etc., as opposed to capitals.

MAKE-READY   ..   The preparatory work done by pressmen before printing to get the best possible results from each individual forme. It consists of measures to obtain an impression of proper strength on every part of the printed area, by putting more or less packing under the type or in the tympan, or, by small patches, to increase the pressure on particular parts of the forme.

MAKE-UP 1 (of a page)   Separating enough type from that on the galley to make a page, adding type for the headings, folios, signatures, initial letters, notes, and spacing material, and tying the metal required for each page together with string.

MAKE-UP 2 (of a book)   Indications given to the printer of what type and illustrations are to appear on each individual page of the book.

MARGINS   ..   ..   The unprinted paper on a page which surrounds the area occupied by the reading matter.

MEASURE   ..   ..   The width of the printed part of a page.

MEDIUM   ..   ..   One of the regular sizes of paper. A full sheet measures 18 × 23 inches. (Double Medium 23 × 36 inches.)

MITRES   ..   ..   Corner-pieces of brass rule which have been cut at an angle of 45 degrees. The object is to get a neat fit at the right angle.

MODERN   ..   ..   A class of roman and italic types with very fine hair lines and serifs used in the last century, now not much used.

NICK   ..   ..   ..   The indentation in the shank of type showing which way up to set it.

OLD-FACE .. .. A class of roman and italic types with triangular serifs and generally of robust appearance dating from about 1480, including for example, Caslon and Cloister.

OPEN TYPE .. .. One having letters with strokes drawn in outline, *e.g.* **E**

OPENING .. .. Two facing pages of a book.

OUT .. .. .. A name for the mistake of leaving out a word or several words of copy in a typesetting.

OVERLAY .. .. To put padding in the tympans of a press to obtain a heavier impression.

OVERRUN .. .. To take a word or more from the end of a line and transfer it to the beginning of the next; or to transfer lines from the end of one page to the beginning of the next.

PAGE .. .. .. 1. A division of the area on one side of a sheet of paper caused by folding.
2. The collection of type and spacing material destined to make the printed impression on a single page of paper.

PAGE-CORD .. .. Fine, strong string tied round pages after they have been made up in the galley. See fig. 13, page 37.

PICA .. .. .. An old size of type corresponding with our 12-pt., used before the introduction of the point-system. A nick-name for 12-pt. still much used by printers. (Pronounced to rhyme with "striker.")

PICK .. .. .. A clot of ink adhering to type.

PICK-BRUSH .. .. A small hand brush used for cleaning type formes.

PIE   ..   ..   ..   An accident in which lines of type become a mass of disorderly confusion.

PLANER   ...   ...   A flat piece of hardwood laid on the face of type and tapped with a mallet to make it stand level before being printed.

PLATEN   ..   ..   The surface which presses the paper against the type during the impression.

POINT   ..   ..   ..   An English typographical point=.01384 of an inch. Used as a unit for measuring the body of types.

PRESS-POINTS   ..   Spikes fixed on the tympan of an Albion press as a means of making register between two or more impressions on a single sheet.

PRESS-PROOF   ..   A proof taken from a forme after it has been laid on the press, as a final precaution against errors in composition and to make sure that the imposition is correct.

PROOF   ..   ..   ..   A trial print from type made for the printer's reader or the author to scrutinise and mark mistakes or alterations on.

PROOF-READING   ..   The business of scrutinising proofs to detect and mark mistakes in composition.

PROOFING PRESS   ..   Any apparatus for impressing inked type on paper for the purpose of judging of the correctness of the type-setting.

QUADS (Quadrats)   ..   Large spaces (from 1 to 4 ems wide) used to fill out blanks and short lines.

QUIRE   ..   ..   ..   Twenty-four sheets of paper.

QUIRED   ..   ..   A sheet folded and inserted in another folded sheet is said to be quired.

QUOINS .. .. .. Wedges of wood or metal used to exert pressure on furniture. They make the type secure within the confines of the chase. (Pronounced as "coins.")

QUOTATIONS .. Another name for metal furniture.

QUOTES .. .. Inverted commas before and apostrophes after a word or phrase, showing that it is quoted or used as a name, etc.

RANDOM .. .. The sloping work-top of a composing frame.

RANGING FIGURES Figures cast so as all to be on a level at top and bottom, *e.g.* 1234567890.

REAM .. .. .. The number of sheets usually done up in a parcel by paper-makers, and forming the normal unit of quantity in the paper trade. A ream of hand-made or writing paper is 480 sheets; a ream of printing paper is 516 sheets.

REGISTER .. .. (1) In printing in two colours, the correct positioning of one colour in relation to the rest of the printing.

(2) In book-work, the placing of the printing on one side of the paper so that it corresponds precisely with the printing on the other side.

REGLET .. .. The narrowest kind of wooden furniture, measuring 6, 12 or 18 points in width.

RIVERS or WINDOWS White streaks appearing in a page of type due to spaces falling immediately above similar spaces in succeeding lines. They are especially likely to occur when spacing between words is too wide.

ROYAL .. .. .. One of the sizes in which paper is made. A full sheet measures 20 × 25 inches. (Double Royal 25 × 40 inches.)

RUN   ..   ..   .. The series of impressions needed to print all the required copies from a forme.

RUNNING-TITLE .. The heading at the top of a page not marking a break in the matter.

SANS (Sans-Serif) .. A style of type-face without serifs. Also called grotesque, doric, or block-letter.

SCRIPT ..   ..   .. Type after the fashion of handwriting.

SERIF   ..   ..   .. An ornamental projection to one side of a stroke of a letter, at top or bottom, showing where the pen begins or ends the stroke.

SET-OFF   ..   .. An impression from wet ink taken off one sheet of paper on to another.

SHANK ..   .·:   .. The rectangular part of a piece of type bearing the letter, etc., at one end.

SHEET ..   ..   .. A whole piece of paper, whether flat or folded.

SHOOTING-STICK ... A piece of metal or hardwood used for driving wooden quoins further into the tapering cavity between a side-stick and the inside of the chase, thus tightening the forme. One end of the shooting-stick is put against the quoin and the other is hit with a mallet.

SIDE-STICK ..   .. A tapered strip of hardwood furniture used in conjunction with wooden quoins to wedge pages of type into the chase. A strip of this kind is used on two sides of every forme, the longer being called the side-stick, and the shorter the end-stick.

SIGNATURE ..   .. A sign, usually a letter, at the bottom of the first page of a sheet showing the binder the sequence of the sheets of a book.

SLUR .. .. .. A smeared or double impression from type.

SOLID .. .. .. Type is said to be set solid if it has no leads between the lines.

SORT .. .. .. A letter, figure, punctuation-mark, sign or other character cast as type.

SPLIT-FRACTIONS Type cast for setting fractions in two parts, one sort bearing the top figure, and the other the bottom figure with the line over it.

SQUABBLE .. .. A group of misprints on a page due to a letter or several letters being pushed out of the proper line into one above or below.

STEREO. (STEREOTYPE) A shallow casting taken from a page of type out of a mould made of papier-maché or plaster of paris.

STOCK .. .. .. The handle and spindle of an ink-roller; that is, the permanent part of it as opposed to the "clothing" of composition which has to be renewed periodically.

STONE .. .. .. Printers often call the imposing-surface "the stone."

SUPERIOR .. .. A sort cast at the top of the body so that it comes above the level of the top of a short letter such as an n. Superior figures are sometimes used as reference-marks.

SWASH LETTERS .. Decorative italic sorts reproducing flourished pen-work, *e.g.*, *A M R N*

TAIL .. .. .. The bottom of a page.

TILL .. .. .. The space between two vertical flanges on top of the platen of a hand-press, commonly used as a receptacle for oddments.

TITLING LETTERS	Capitals cast so as to occupy the whole of the body, leaving no beard at the foot.
TURN	To use a sort feet-uppermost temporarily in the place of one not available.
TWEEZERS	Forceps for picking type out of the forme.
TYMPAN	The paper packing on the platen of a printing machine, or the steel frames covered with parchment and containing padding hinged to the bed of an Albion press.
TYPE-HIGH	Of the same height as type. English type is 0.917 of an inch high.
UNDERLAY	To put packing between the bed of the press and the feet of the type.
WRONG FOUNT ..	A mistake in composition consisting of using a letter of the wrong size or not of the same design as the rest.

APPENDIX 2
SOME SPECIMEN
SETTINGS

13 St. Augustus Road
Framlingham, Suffolk
Tetephone 104

SET IN 12-PT. AND 10-PT. BASKERVILLE

Telephone: Stone 14 HIGH HOUSE SCHOOL
CLAYDON, RUTLAND

SET IN 10-PT. CLOISTER

"THE FIRS"
TADCASTER TERRACE
PONTEFRACT

Some settings for letter-paper (reduced in scale)

LE PETIT POISSON ET LE PECHEUR

Petit poisson deviendra grand,

Pourvu que Dieu lui prête vie.

Mais le lâcher en attendant

Je tiens pour moi que c'est folie:

Car de le rattraper il n'est pas trop certain.

Un carpeau, qui n'était encore que fretin,

Fut pris par un pêcheur au bord d'une rivière,

"Tout fait nombre, di l'homme, en voyant son butin;

Voilà commencement de chère & de festin:

Mettons-le en notre gibecière."

Le pauvre carpillon lui dit en sa manière:

"Que ferez-vous de moi? Je ne saurais fournir

A specimen setting of poetry to illustrate optical centreing and wide leading

The Cartwright Hall

DUFFIELD-ON-WHARFE

==

*A*n exhibition of poker-work and leather bookbindings will be held in the EAST WING during September & October. All are cordially invited. The exhibition will remain open on each day until sundown.

==

¶ Admittance free, including Sundays

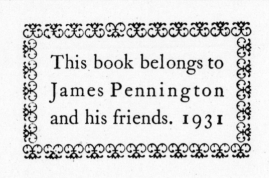

This book belongs to
James Pennington
and his friends. 1931

WORTING HIGH SCHOOL

EXERCISE
BOOK

SUBJECT...

A book-plate and book-label.

CRICKET FIXTURES

SUMMER TERM

H=*Home*   A=*Away*

H	Broadwater	.	May 6th
A	Mr. Dent's XI	.	May 13th
H	Berchiston	.	May 20th
A	King Edward's	.	June 3rd
H	Mr. Boswell's XI	.	June 10th
H	PARENTS' MATCH	.	June 17th
A	Grace House	.	June 24th
H	Barchester Clergy	.	July 1st
H	Vernham Dene	.	July 15th
A	Mr. Pye's XI	.	July 22nd

Inside

CRICKET FIXTURES

MONK SHERBORNE SCHOOL

Front Cover

THE WHITE HOUSE SCHOOL LIBRARY

Title...

Card Index Number

Name   *Date Out*

138

BIBLIOGRAPHY

JACOBI, C. T. *Printing*. Geo. Bell & Sons. 1919.

JACOBI, C. T. *Some Notes on Books and Printing*. Chiswick Press. 1903.

MORISON, S. *The Art of the Printer*. Benn. 1925.
[Reproductions of printed pages dating from 1500-1900.]

MORISON, S. *On Type Faces*. Medici Society. 1923.

DE VINNE, T. I.. *Modern Methods of Book Composition*. Oswald Publishing Co., New York. 1914.

THORP, J. *Printing for Business*. John Hogg, Paternoster Row. 1919.

SLATER, W. H. *What a Compositor Should Know*. Borough Publishing Co. 3 vols.

ALDIS, H. G. *The Printed Book*. Cambridge University Press.

Printing in the 20th Century: "The Times" Printing Number. "The Times" Publishing Co. 1929.

SIMON, O., AND RODENBERG, J. *Printing of To-day*. Peter Davies. 1928.

UPDIKE, D. B. *Printing Types, Their History, Forms and Use*. Harvard University Press. 1923.

Printing: A Short History. Edited by R. A. PEDDIE. Grafton & Co. 1927.

AUDIN, M. *Histoire de l'Imprimerie par l'Image*. Jonquiéres, Paris. 1928. 4 vols.

LEGROS, A., AND GRANT, J. C. *Typographical Printing Surfaces*. Longmans, Green & Co. 1916.

Report of the Committee Appointed to Select the Best Faces of Type and Modes of Display for Government Printing. H.M. Stationery Office. 1922.

CURWEN, H. *Processes of Graphic Reproduction in Printing*. Faber & Faber. 1934.

SEABY, A. W. *Colour Printing with Linoleum and Wood Blocks*. Dryad Press.

HEWITT BATES, J. S. *Bookbinding for Schools*. Dryad Press. 1945

TANNER, R. *Children's Work in Block Printing*. Dryad Press. 1942

MASON, J. *Gold and Colour Tooling for Bookbinding*. Dryad Press.

Linoleum Cutting and Printing. Dryad Press.

SIMON, O. *Introduction to Typography*. Faber & Faber. 1945.

INDEX

INDEX (*Continued*)

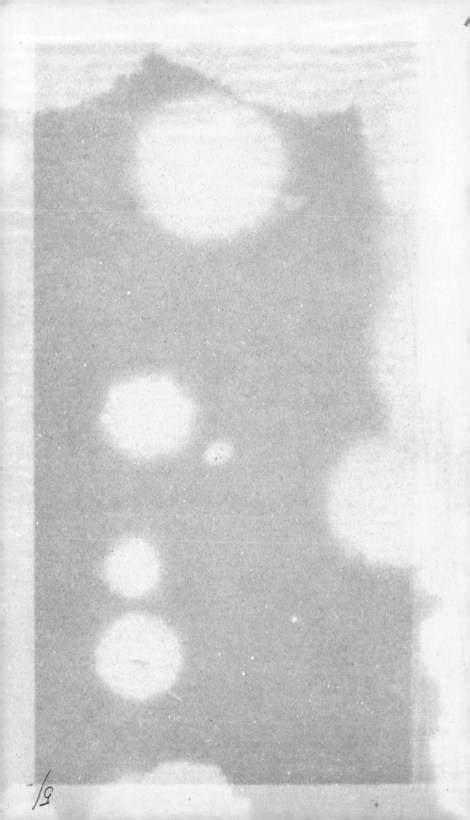